Here's all the great literature in this grade level of *Celebrate Reading!*

Don't Wake the Princess

Hopes, Dreams, and Wishes

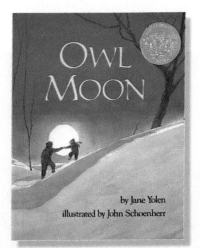

Owl Moon
by Jane Yolen
Illustrations by John Schoenherr
✳ Kerlan Award Author
✳ Caldecott Medal

Sleeping Ugly
by Jane Yolen

Lentil
by Robert McCloskey
✳ Caldecott Medal Illustrator

Jacob Lawrence: Painter of the American Scene
by Kathleen Stevens

The River That Gave Gifts
by Margo Humphrey

The Flame of Peace
retold by Deborah Nourse Lattimore
✳ Notable Social Studies Trade Book

Harry Kitten and Tucker Mouse
from the novel by George Selden
Illustrations by Garth Williams
✳ Newbery Honor Author

The Dog That Pitched a No-Hitter
by Matt Christopher

The Turtle Who Wanted to Fly
retold as a play by Carol Korty

Featured Poet
Jane Yolen

The World Is Round Just Like an Orange

Many Ways of Learning

Teacher's Pet
from the novel by Johanna Hurwitz
✸ Garden State Children's Book Award

Cheating
by Susan Shreve

There's a Boy in the Girls' Bathroom
from the novel by Louis Sachar
✸ Children's Choice

Pop Goes the Popcorn
retold by Virginia C. Holmgren

Beezus and Ramona
from the novel by Beverly Cleary
✸ Newbery Medal Author

Yani's Monkeys
by Scarlet Cheng

Ride the Red Cycle
by Harriette Gillem Robinet

My Backyard History
from the book by David Weitzman

Featured Poets
Ann Turner
Myra Cohn Livingston

We're All in This Together

How Families Matter

Yagua Days
by Cruz Martel
Illustrations by Jerry Pinkney
* Notable Social Studies Trade Book
* Reading Rainbow Selection

I'm the Big Sister Now
by Michelle Emmert

My Adopted Grandpa
by Amie Wortman

Childtimes
from the autobiography by
Eloise Greenfield
* Boston Globe-Horn Book Award
* Irma Simonton Black Award

No One Is Going to Nashville
by Mavis Jukes
Illustrations by Lloyd Bloom
* *School Library Journal* Best Book
* Irma Simonton Black Award

We Don't Look Like Our
Mom and Dad
by Harriet Langsam Sobol

A Day with the Amish
by Linda Egenes

Featured Poet
Eloise Greenfield

Y.O.U.

(Your Own Universe)

The Kid in the Red Jacket
from the novel by Barbara Park
✳ Children's Choice

Between Old Friends
from the book by Katherine Leiner

China's Precious Pandas
by Claire Miller

**And It Is Still That Way:
Legends Told by Arizona
Indian Children**
collected by Byrd Baylor
✳ Boston Globe-Horn Book
Award Author

**Who's the New Kid with
the Hoofs? (or) Mary Had
a Little Problem**
by Martha Bolton

Turtle Watch
by George Ancona
✳ ALA Notable Children's Book
✳ Notable Social Studies Trade Book
✳ Outstanding Science Trade Book

On the Banks of Plum Creek
from the novel by
Laura Ingalls Wilder
Illustrations by Garth Williams
✳ Newbery Honor Book

Addie Across the Prairie
from the novel by Laurie Lawlor

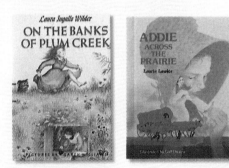

Featured Poets
Nikki Giovanni
Philip Whalen

Do You Hear What I See?

Looking at the World in New Ways

**Something Queer in
Rock 'n' Roll**
by Elizabeth Levy

The Crow and the Pitcher
retold by Tom Paxton
✹ Notable Social Studies Trade Book
✹ *School Library Journal* Best Book

How to Weigh an Elephant
retold by Frances Alexander

Bo Rabbit Smart for True
retold by Priscilla Jaquith
Illustrations by Ed Young
✹ Caldecott Medal Illustrator

Mother Goose Gumshoe
by Christina Hamlett

Family Pictures
by Carmen Lomas Garza

**Faith Ringgold's
Stories in Art**
by Leslie Sills

The Boll Weevil
Illustrated by Glen Rounds

**Mr. Yowder and the
Train Robbers**
by Glen Rounds
✹ Parents' Choice Award Illustrator
✹ Lewis Carroll Shelf Award Author

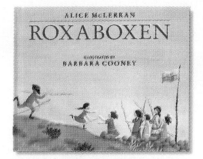

Roxaboxen
by Alice McLerran
Illustrations by Barbara Cooney
✹ Caldecott Medal Illustrator

**Round Buildings, Square
Buildings, and Buildings That
Wiggle Like a Fish**
from the book by Philip M. Isaacson
✹ Notable Social Studies Trade Book
✹ Boston Globe-Horn Book Award

Featured Poets
David McCord
Virginia Driving Hawk Sneve

The Wolf Is at the Door
Tales of Courage

Night of the Twisters
by Ivy Ruckman
✷ Children's Choice

A Leak in the Dike
by Paul T. Nolan

Night Dive
from the book by Ann McGovern

Teammates
by Peter Golenbock
✷ Notable Social Studies Trade Book

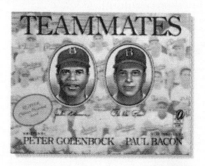

Nadia the Willful
by Sue Alexander
Illustrations by Lloyd Bloom
✷ Teachers' Choice

Atariba & Niguayona
retold by Harriet Rohmer and
Jesús Guerrero Rea

**Lon Po Po: A Red-Riding
Hood Story from China**
translated and illustrated
by Ed Young
✷ Caldecott Medal
✷ ALA Notable Children's Book

Featured Poets
John Ciardi
Emily Hearn
Aileen Fisher

Celebrate Reading!
Trade Books

Bicycle Rider
by Mary Scioscia
✺ Notable Social Studies Trade Book

Sarah, Plain and Tall
by Patricia MacLachlan
✺ Newbery Medal
✺ ALA Notable Children's Book
✺ *School Library Journal* Best Book
✺ Children's Choice
✺ *New York Times* Notable
Children's Book

Shoeshine Girl
by Clyde Robert Bulla
✺ Sequoyah Children's Book Award
✺ South Carolina Children's
Book Award
✺ Southern California Council on
Literature for Children Award

**There's a Boy in the Girls'
Bathroom**
by Louis Sachar
✺ Children's Choice
✺ Young Readers' Choice

Talk About a Family
by Eloise Greenfield

**Tales of a Fourth
Grade Nothing**
by Judy Blume
✺ Children's Choice
✺ Young Readers' Choice
✺ Sequoyah Children's Book Award

Charlotte's Web
by E. B. White
✺ Newbery Medal
✺ Lewis Carroll Shelf Award

Staying Nine
by Pam Conrad
✺ Children's Editors' Choice

A Clue in Code
by Marilyn Singer

**The Mouse and the
Motorcycle**
by Beverly Cleary
✺ ALA Notable Children's Book
✺ Young Readers' Choice

Stone Fox
by John Reynolds Gardiner
✺ Maud Hart Lovelace Book Award
✺ Southern California Council on
Literature for Children Award

Sidewalk Story
by Sharon Bell Mathis
✺ Council on Interracial Books Award

TALES OF COURAGE

Titles in This Set

Don't Wake the Princess

The World Is Round
Just Like an Orange

We're All in This Together

Y.O.U.

Do You Hear What I See?

The Wolf Is at the Door

About the Cover Artist
Bob Gleason has designed and illustrated movie
posters, greeting cards, and record album covers—
including one for Stevie Wonder. This cover is his
first illustration for a textbook.

ISBN 0-673-81153-0

1997
Scott, Foresman and Company, Glenview, Illinois
All Rights Reserved.
Printed in the United States of America.

CELEBRATE READING! ® is a registered
trademark of Scott, Foresman and Company.

Acknowledgments appear on page 144.

2345678910DQ010099989796

The Wolf Is at the Door

TALES OF COURAGE

 ScottForesman

A Division of HarperCollins*Publishers*

Contents

Take a Deep Breath

Night of the Twisters   F•7
Realistic fiction by Ivy Ruckman

A Word from the Author   F•33
Essay by Ivy Ruckman

About the Teeth of Sharks   F•39
Poem by John Ciardi

Courage   F•40
Poem by Emily Hearn

In the Dark of Night   F•41
Poem by Aileen Fisher

A Leak in the Dike   F•43
Play by Paul T. Nolan

Ready, Set, Dive!   F•61
from Night Dive
Nonfiction by Ann McGovern

What Would You Do?

Teammates   F•75
Expository nonfiction by Peter Golenbock

A Word from the Author   F•83
Essay by Peter Golenbock

Nadia the Willful   F•87
Realistic fiction by Sue Alexander
Illustrations by Lloyd Bloom

A Word from the Author   F•103
Personal essay by Sue Alexander

Courage in Folk Tales
GENRE STUDY

Atariba & Niguayona   F•107
Folk tale retold by Harriet Rohmer
and Jesús Guerrero Rea

Lon Po Po: A Red-Riding Hood Story
from China   F•121
Folk tale translated and illustrated by Ed Young

Student Resources
Books to Enjoy   F•134
Literary Terms   F•136
Glossary   F•138

NIGHT OF THE TWISTERS

BY IVY RUCKMAN

GRAND ISLAND, NEB., JUNE 4 (AP) — A string of seven tornadoes devastated this central Nebraska city last night, killing four persons and injuring 134.

Initial reports said five persons were killed, and one county official said this morning that she thought more than 30 bodies had been found. . . .

The city was battered by the tornadoes over a three-hour period. When they were over, a six-block-wide swath along Grand Island's two main streets was devastated.

The Federal Emergency Management Administration said that 513 homes and 60 businesses had been destroyed. In addition, 450 homes and 15 businesses were damaged. . . .

Radar indicated that the tornadoes that hit Grand Island were touched off by a thunderstorm cell at least 35 miles wide that formed shortly before 8 P.M.

Associated Press, June 4, 1980

**I**SN'T IT FUNNY how you remember all the crummy little details on one of those black-letter days? My folks say it was that way with them the day President Kennedy was shot way back in 1963. And Belle Smiley, the oldest person in our neighborhood, said she could still remember exactly where she was and what she was thinking on Pearl Harbor Day.

My all-time worst black-letter day was June third of last summer. There were no notices mailed out on that occasion, for sure. There were no indications at all.

"Twenty percent probability of thunderstorms toward evening" was what the local weatherman said that morning.

"So what's new?" Mom talked back to him, poking another spoonful of cereal in my baby brother's smiling mouth.

To tell you the truth, the weather was the last thing on my mind. Arthur and I had big plans for that Tuesday. Crafts class first, at my Aunt Goldie's place. A couple of hot burritos at Taco John's after. Later, a bike hike out to the Platte River and a swim at Mormon Island.

As Arthur and I pedaled off that day there were no warnings at all. None. I remember the bottom-heavy look of the sky and those strong blasts of air that hit us going home.

I can even tell you what we had for supper on that June the third. All I have to do to recall the wonderful smell of our kitchen that night is to close my eyes and inhale. Mom had just taken a chocolate meringue pie out of the oven.

"Can Arthur eat with us?" I asked.

"If he calls his mother," she said matter-of-factly.

Before Ryan was born, Mom used to call Arthur and me her twins, meaning my buddy and I were practically inseparable. Of course, Arthur has dark skin and a mop of wavy black hair, whereas I'm one of those yellow-haired, freckle-faced types. He's short and fat; I'm not. We could never pass for brothers, let alone twins, because we're different in other ways too. He's a thinker; I'm a doer. He's crazy about books; I go bonkers over bikes. Just the same, we consider ourselves blood relatives, and that's what counts.

As Arthur stepped to the wall phone and dialed, Mom gave me a sideways look that meant *Why don't you clear things with me first?*

I just lifted an extra glass and plate off the shelf and pretended not to notice.

After dinner, Arthur and I flipped on the TV.

"Channel five or ten?" I asked.

"Ten."

I moved his feet and sat down next to him.

The TV show had already started, but that rarely bothers Arthur and me. When we're watching something funny we can tune in any old time.

During the first commercial, I went to the kitchen for potato chips.

When I returned, Arthur was so glad for the arrival of food that we almost missed the severe-weather announcement.

". . . in the St. Paul area, just north of Grand Island . . ."

Mom rushed into the living room. "Listen!" She shushed us.

". . . in effect until further notice is given. Funnel clouds have been sighted near St. Paul, Dannebrog, and surrounding rural areas."

"Do we have to go to the basement?" I asked. Now that we were all set for the next show, I hoped not.

Mom didn't answer. She had her face right up against our big front window, shielding her eyes, trying to see out. Normally she's a lot more casual about storms. But Dad was out at my grandpa's farm fixing a tractor. I knew she was worried he'd get caught in a tornado on the way home.

"It's pitch-black out there," she said. "I've never seen it so dark this early."

It was noisy outside as well. Our shake shingles, flapping and smacking overhead, made me think somebody was up there playing a xylophone. Minerva, our cat, didn't like the weather either. She was crouched under Dad's chair with her ears back.

"Do we have to go downstairs?" I asked again.

"Not yet, Danny. We'll keep listening to the TV."

Arthur spoke up, "Tornadoes move from

southwest to northeast, remember?"

I remembered. Our science class had taken a field trip to visit the weather service out at the airport.

Arthur made arm motions toward a plant hanging in the corner of the room. "It'll head off that way some place."

Arthur has books on everything— birds, trees, flowers, insects, amphibians, prunes, tornadoes. So, his expert opinion should have made me feel better, but it didn't.

He helped himself to another potato chip, then settled back into the cushions. *He* wasn't worried.

We watched TV another few minutes, but I couldn't get into it. Not that I was scared, exactly. I'd been through dozens of tornado watches in my life and nothing ever happened. Every spring, practically, we have to "hit for the cellar," as Grandpa puts it. But when a tornado watch changes to a warning, and when the siren starts . . . well . . . that's when things aren't so mellow any more.

Next thing I knew, Mom was at the hall closet, putting her red windbreaker on over her jeans.

"I'm driving over to check on old Mrs. Smiley," she said. "She doesn't answer her phone. She's probably turned that hearing aid down again and won't have her TV on. Now listen, both of you."

We listened. She was using a very firm voice.

"I want you to take the flashlight and a blanket and put them in the downstairs bathroom. I want you to do it *this minute!*"

I nodded.

"If the siren starts, get Ryan and go downstairs. Don't wake him up if you can help it, all right?"

Arthur's eyes got big listening to Mom. He told me once they never go to the basement during windstorms. That figures. They moved here from California, what do they know? Ever hear of a tornado in good old CA?

"I'll be right back," Mom told us. "I'm sure nothing's going to happen, but we have to be prepared, right?" She smiled and waved her car keys at us as she left, barely squeezing out before the door slammed shut again.

*HOOEEEEE!"* Arthur exclaimed. "Listen to that wind!"

I hurried downstairs with the emergency stuff and set it on the bathroom counter. Minerva went with me, scurrying across my feet, acting the way she does when she wants attention. I picked her up by the middle, but she just gave me her mean jungle look.

Upstairs, Arthur was hooting and hollering again. I was missing all the good parts, so I hurried up the two short flights of steps, with Minerva dashing ahead of me.

Sometime in there, in the middle of all that comedy on the screen, the siren began. Now, *that* is a very sobering sound. It's unlike anything else, having its own built-in chill factor.

I thought of Mom first. She'd hear it and come back, I told myself.

Then I thought of Grandma and Grandpa and Dad and how far the farm was from town. They wouldn't even hear the siren out there.

In half a second I was at the phone. Four rings, then I heard Grandma's voice.

"Grandma!" I shouted into the phone. "There's a tornado just north of G.I. The siren's going, can you hear it?"

A voice said something, but it sounded so far away. "Talk louder, Grandma! I can't hear you."

The voice faded away entirely.

"There's a tornado coming! Can you hear me?"

There wasn't anything on the line now but the sound of another phone ringing faintly, as if it were in New York or someplace far away.

By then, Arthur was standing next to me. I was just about to hand him the phone when, abruptly, the siren stopped. It didn't taper off, it just quit, as if someone snipped it with scissors. Except for the TV, everything around us suddenly seemed very still.

"Hey," he said, raising his eyebrows, "they changed their minds."

I hung up the phone and ran to the door, thinking I might see Mom pulling into the driveway, but no luck.

"It's quit blowing," I called over my shoulder to Arthur.

Sure enough, the wind had died down. Maybe the storm wouldn't amount to anything after all.

That nice comforting thought had hardly entered my mind when the siren blared forth again. With a jolt, I remembered what Mom had told us to do.

"L ET'S TURN ON THE RADIO," Arthur said.

I hurried down the hallway to Ryan's room. I hated to get him up. I knew he'd wake up and cry. Without Mom, Arthur and I would have him screaming in our ears the whole time.

When I saw him in his crib, peacefully sleeping, his rear end in the air, I just didn't have the heart to wake him up. I'd wait a minute or two. Mom would be back. Anyway, it's blowing over, I told myself.

Quietly, I closed the door. That's when the lights started flickering.

In the hallway, I practically had a head-on with Arthur, who was coming at me real fast. The look on his face scared me.

"There's no . . . there's no . . ."

"What?"

"There's no radio reception any more. It just went dead! This guy . . . He kept saying, 'Tornado alert, tornado alert!' Then it went dead."

We rushed back to the living room. The TV was flashing these big letters that filled the entire screen: CD . . . CD . . . CD.

"What's it mean?" Arthur cried.

"Civil Defense Emergency!" I whirled around. "I'm getting Ryan!"

 *SMASHED FACE FIRST* into Ryan's butterfly mobile. That's how I knew I was at the crib. I felt for him and lifted him out, but we didn't get far. He was caught in the mobile, his arm or his head; I couldn't see, I couldn't get him loose.

"Mom!" I yelled, though I knew she wasn't there. I grabbed the mobile and pulled it from the ceiling.

The tornado was close, and I knew it. Both my ears had popped, and all the drains in the house were sucking like monsters.

Arthur was at the bottom of the stairs, waiting. Thank God he'd found the flashlight! I jumped the last half-flight to the floor.

"Hurry!" I screamed. I swung into the doorway of the bathroom, with Arthur right behind me. We crawled into the shower and sat on the floor.

"Shine it here, on Ryan," I gasped. "He's caught in this thing." By now Ryan was kicking and screaming, and his eyes were big in the light.

Once we got the mess of strings free of Ryan's sweaty nightshirt, Arthur kicked the mobile against the wall by the toilet.

"I have to go home!" he cried. "They won't go to the basement. Mama never does."

The beam of light bounced around the blackness of the bathroom as Arthur scrambled to his feet, but I grabbed and held on to him.

"You can't go! It's here! Can't you feel it?"

The siren quit again as I pulled him back down and threw my leg over him. The flashlight clattered to the floor and rolled away from us.

We heard it next. The lull. The deadliest quiet ever, one that makes you think you might explode. The heat in the room built until I couldn't get my breath.

Then I began to hear noises. A chair scraping across the kitchen floor upstairs.

"Your mom's back!" Arthur said, pushing at my leg.

I knew it wasn't my mother moving the chair.

The noises got worse. It seemed as if every piece of furniture was moving around up there . . . big, heavy things, smashing into each other.

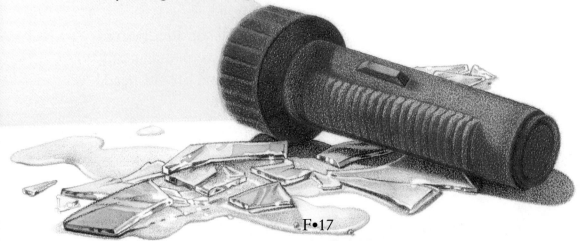

A window popped.

Crash! Another.

Glass, shattered everywhere.

I pulled a towel down over Ryan and held him tight. If he was still crying, I didn't know it because I was *feeling* the sucking this time. It was like something trying to lift my body right up off the floor.

Arthur felt it too. "Mother of God!" he crossed himself. "We're going to die!"

Ten seconds more and that howling, shrieking tornado was upon us.

"The blanket!" I screamed at Arthur's ear.

We covered ourselves, hands shaking wildly. I wasn't worrying about my mom then or my dad or Mrs. Smiley. Just us. Ryan and Arthur and me, huddled together there on the shower floor.

The roaring had started somewhere to the east, then came bearing down on us like a hundred freight trains. Only that twister didn't move on. It stationed itself right overhead, making the loudest noise I'd ever heard, whining worse than any jet. There was a tremendous crack, and I felt the wall shudder behind us. I knew then our house was being ripped apart. Suddenly chunks of ceiling were falling on our heads. We'll be buried! was all I could think.

We pulled the blanket over our heads, and I began to pray. Out loud, though I couldn't hear my own voice: "God help us, God help us." I said it over and over into Ryan's damp hair, my lips moving against his head. I knew Arthur was praying too, jammed there into my side. I could feel Ryan's heart beating through his undershirt against mine. There was nothing but terror as the roar of that tornado went on and on. I thought the world was coming to an end. And so would we, any minute.

Then I felt Ryan's fat fingers close around one of mine. He pulled my hand to his mouth and started sucking on my finger. It made me cry. The tears ran down my cheeks and onto his head. With the whole world blowing to pieces around us, Ryan took my hand and made me feel better.

"A tornado's forward speed is generally thirty to fifty miles an hour," a meteorologist had told us.

Our tornado's forward speed was zero. Five minutes or ten, we couldn't tell, but it seemed like an hour. Roaring and humming and shrieking, that twister was right on top of us. I'll never be that scared again as long as I live. Neither will Arthur.

WHEN AT LAST the noise began to let up, Arthur jerked out from under the blanket, leaned across me to the opening of the shower, and vomited into the broken glass and Sheetrock.

Squeamish as I am about something like that, I wasn't revolted. I wondered if I had wet my pants myself. I couldn't tell for sure because water had started rising under us in the shower. My shoes and jeans were both soaked.

"Arthur," I said, my voice shaking, but thinking to encourage him, "we made it . . . we're alive!"

But then the hail began. Once it got going, it hit us with the force of buckshot. Those marble-size hailstones were pouring in from above somewhere. I knew then that the kitchen was gone, floor and all.

It didn't take long for Arthur to crawl back beside me, but even under the blanket those hailstones hurt like crazy, smacking our heads and shoulders. We moved together to protect Ryan.

Suddenly I was hit with a sickness worse than Arthur's. Mom! Where was she? Did she get to Mrs. Smiley's?

"Arthur!" I cried, sitting up straight. "My mom!"

"My . . . whole family," he choked out.

In that second I could see my mother's car hurtling through the air, see it ripping open, the black funnel sucking her out and swirling her away. I could hear her *scream!*

I started crying. "She can't be dead, she can't be!" I hit my head against the tile to make the pictures stop.

"Shut up!" Arthur shouted. "Just shut up, will you?"

He pulled away so we weren't touching and drew himself into the opposite corner of the shower. I didn't care. I felt as if someone had reached down my throat and turned me inside out.

Chills raced up my arms. I was shaking all over.

At least, I scrabbled for something to hang on to, *at least I still have my dad!* He'd be safe, wouldn't he, out on the farm?

I clenched my teeth to keep from going to pieces. "Please, God, please," I begged, "make everyone O.K.!"

Overhead, the storm continued to rage. The sharp sound of hail striking tile went on and on, and I began to wonder if we might just be battered to death. I shuddered and pulled up my knees, shifting the baby once more. With the temperature dropping and the water rising, we couldn't stay in the shower stall forever. What were we going to do?

Only Ryan had recovered enough to be himself and was dabbling one hand in the water, making noises. Once I got him in a standing position against my knees, he began "talking" and stretching under the blanket tent. *He* wasn't worried.

Suddenly it occurred to me that I had saved his life. I *had!* I warmed myself on that thought as I rubbed my cheek against his head.

That was when I remembered Minerva. My cat! Oh, no! Had she followed us downstairs? But a cat would find a place—wouldn't she?—to ride out the storm. Cats are smart. They can take care of themselves.

The hard peppering sounds of the hail were growing slushier, softer. The hail was turning to rain. Quickly I slipped the blanket off my head.

My gosh!

There was the night sky where the bathroom ceiling had been! I shivered as icy raindrops splatted in my face and went streaking down my neck. Somehow, *seeing* was worse than knowing.

"Arthur—" I nudged him with my foot, "— look up there!"

"Listen," Arthur said, now that things had quieted a little, "do you hear water running?"

I'd been hearing it: water gurgling and splashing onto the cement floor.

"Pipes are broken," he said.

"Let's go," I said through chattering teeth, though I didn't have any idea where.

Arthur got out ahead of me, carefully picking his way across the bathroom rubble. He held up something shiny—our towel rack, bent like a boomerang. With that he dug among chunks of Sheetrock for the flashlight, which miraculously was still on.

I stood up with Ryan in my arms. He patted my face. He was as glad to be up and moving as I was.

The first shock was Arthur's, because he had the flashlight. When I pushed into the doorway beside him, I caught my breath. Our house was gone. Roof, walls, floor—gone! Inside the foundation—surrounding us and blocking our way—was a jungle of fallen support beams and splintered wood.

I couldn't speak. I just stood there, letting the horrible truth soak in.

"The stairs must be buried too," I said finally.

Arthur climbed up onto the arm of Dad's easy chair, which was now in the bathroom doorway. He covered the west foundation from one end to the other with the light.

"Dan, maybe we could climb out over that pile of bricks on the other side."

Just then a low, moaning sound raised hackles on the back of my neck. Arthur jumped off the chair. We froze. The noise rumbled to a crescendo right over our heads, making us jump when it crashed. Thunder! My lord, it was only thunder!

"Take Ryan a minute," I said, recovering enough to trade him for the flashlight. "I'll give it a try."

I left them at the bathroom door and snaked my way alongside the hallway, ducking and burrowing under debris when I had to. Glass crunched underfoot with every step, and I kept getting snagged by things I couldn't see.

The biggest hurdle was a mass of wet carpeting— gold shag from our living room. I pushed against it. It was too soggy, too heavy. I'd have to crawl over.

"Ow, ouch!" I cried as something gouged me in the leg.

"You O.K.?" Arthur yelled.

"I'm O.K.," I answered back. My jeans were ripped, and I was bleeding, but the wound wasn't mortal, as Arthur would say. I stood there a minute, breathing hard, wondering what to do next. It was raining again, and I was shaking—from the cold, from being so scared. I wanted my mom and dad so much!

I slid down on my heels, pushing my face into the wet carpet. Hot tears squeezed out of my eyes. What in the world was I supposed to do?

D AN, WHAT'S GOING ON?" Arthur called, and I remembered I'd left him in the dark. I turned around and went crashing back to Arthur and Ryan.

"We can't get through," I said with fresh panic.

I took Ryan and held him close, rocking and shushing him the way I'd seen Mom do it. He snuggled into my chest. He didn't know it, but he was warming me as much as I was warming him.

Just then a light appeared overhead, bobbing up and down with someone's steps.

"HELP!" Arthur yelled at once. "We're down here!"

"*Arthur!* Dear God, is that you?"

Hope shot through me like an electric charge. Arthur was jumping up and down. "Stacey?"

It was Arthur's sister. He shot the light straight up in the sky, waving it around like a beacon.

Seconds later, Stacey was looking down on us from above, and we were lighting up each other's faces, which didn't need lighting up at all. We would have glowed in the dark, we were so glad to see each other.

"Where's Mama? Is she O.K.? What about— "

"Everyone's O.K., now that I've found *you!*"

For the first time, Arthur burst into tears. Big sobs racked his body. He couldn't have held them back if he'd tried.

"I thought you were all . . . *dead!*" Arthur gulped. "I didn't think you'd go downstairs."

"Oh, Arthur, we didn't! There wasn't time. We had to flatten out on the floor—it was awful! We were lying there, holding each other, Arthur— " Her voice broke. "Ronnie Vae got sucked right out the window."

I gasped.

"I tried to hang on to her, but I couldn't. I couldn't do anything but scream."

"Stacey! Is she all right?"

"She is! It's a pure miracle! It threw her into the bushes, knocked her right out."

I shuddered. I could feel that sucking tornado all over again, I could see Ronnie—

Ryan let out a first-class wail about then that sent all of us into action. Stacey leaned over the foundation and spotted the toilet tank with her big flashlight.

"Listen, Dan," she said, gulping hard, "can you climb up on that john with Ryan?"

I nodded.

"Hand the baby up to me first," she said, "then I'll help you guys."

Our yard looked like a World War II battlefield. Next to the flattened garage, Dad's prized white Corvette lay on its top like a discarded matchbox toy. Somewhere under that trash heap was my bike. My beloved ten-speed racer.

"The whole neighborhood's gone," Stacey said. Wreckage was scattered in every direction as far as we could see. Stacey handed me the torch so she could snap her dad's big denim jacket around Ryan.

"Stacey, I have to find my mom," I blurted out suddenly.

"What do you mean? Don't you *know* where she is?"

I could feel the corners of my mouth pulling down. I turned away, so Arthur had to tell her about Mom leaving to check on Mrs. Smiley. Then he asked Stacey if she could take Ryan to their house so the two of us could go look for Mom.

"Arthur!" she exclaimed. "We don't have a house any more!"

His jaw dropped. "We don't?"

"All that's left is a few walls. The whole neighborhood looks like this."

It was Arthur's turn to be speechless. I know how sick it sounds, but somehow hearing such bad news made me feel better. We were all in the same boat.

"Where's Mama now?" Arthur asked.

"Patrol cars were down at the end of the block loading people up. I begged her to let me come to

Dan's and look for you. She said if I found you, we should get out fast. It's too dangerous to stay here."

I stopped right in front of her. "I'm not leaving without my mom!"

"Of course not, Dan. We'll find her. I'll bet she's waiting out the storm at Mrs. Smiley's right now."

A blast of wind plastered my wet clothes to my body, triggering a bad case of the shakes. I prayed to God Stacey was right.

Once we got to the street, we took off running. Covering those three blocks was like reliving my worst nightmare. Rain-soaked, shaken by thunder that rolled across the sky like kettledrums, I kept telling myself I'd wake up and laugh because none of it was true. It was just too terrible, that's all.

All structures—houses, garages, fences, telephone poles—had been leveled, the debris scattered helter-skelter. The trees looked as if some giant with a big, meaty hand had stripped the main branches and snapped off the rest.

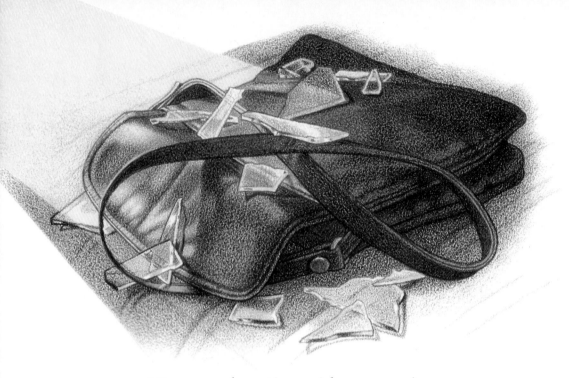

We went a long time without stopping—
stumbling, ducking things that were blowing loose.
We were so intent on sweeping both sides of the street
with our lights, we sometimes crashed into each other
in the dark.

"Mom . . . *Mom!*" I tried yelling at first, but the
wind shredded my words.

When I saw Mom's car, my heart quit beating
altogether. It was a battered wreck wrapped in a
length of chain-link fence.

"*Mom!*" I screamed, clambering over everything
to get to it. My hands shook wildly as I shone the
light inside. Her purse lay on the front seat, covered
with broken glass.

"Mom . . . Mom!" I cried, frantically hauling stuff
out from under the car. Boards and bricks and chunks
of siding, throwing them anywhere, digging and
crying until I couldn't see. I had to find her!

Arthur grabbed my arm from behind. "Come on,
Dan," he yelled. "She made it to Mrs. Smiley's,
I know she did!"

I shook him off. I had to find her.

Then the two of them got hold of me and pulled me away from the car. I kicked at Stacey, swore at Arthur, but they wouldn't let go. I knew she was there, buried under that car, I *knew* it.

I was so crazy right then I didn't see the person in the red windbreaker hurrying toward us. Seconds later, I was in my mother's arms crying like a baby. Arthur and Stacey were crying too, but Mom and I were the ones making most of the noise. We all had our arms around each other next. Mom was kissing everybody.

HERE WERE MORE tornadoes that night in Grand Island. In fact, six or seven tornadoes hit our city. Our cat, Minerva, never did show up. I guess a lightweight kitty couldn't survive those winds. But we found Dad early the next morning. Our whole family danced around, hugging and kissing each other. I knew right then that nothing else mattered. You can do without all kinds of things—your house, your bike, your room, a whole city of people—if you have the ones you love.

WRITING

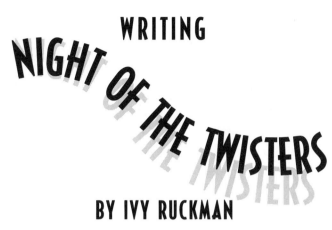

NIGHT OF THE TWISTERS

BY IVY RUCKMAN

JUNE 4, 1980, SALT LAKE CITY. I was on my way home and had just turned on the car radio for some news. Hearing the word *Nebraska*, I sat up and listened. A series of severe tornadoes had hit the city of Grand Island the night before.

"Thirty to thirty-five people are believed dead," said the announcer.

I stepped on the gas. A favorite cousin and her family lived in Grand Island. I had been to visit them only three weeks before.

Please, not Florence! I remember thinking as I raced home to the phone.

No luck. The lines were down. Finally, ten days later, Florence Rozendal was able to reach me.

"We lived through it," she said, "but we lost everything—car, house, furniture. All but the microwave oven."

She laughed nervously at that point, but I was covered with goosebumps. I asked a hundred questions, eager to hear every detail.

Two years later, when the goosebumps

wouldn't go away, I began to write *Night of the Twisters*, a novel for young readers.

Once in the grip of an idea, I find it best to be a good listener. I must "hear" whatever comes bubbling up from inside. I also begin "seeing" scenes in my head, imagining what might happen *if.* Again and again, I thought about my cousin's terrifying night. I tried hard to imagine how it would be to start over with only the clothes on one's back. Deep down inside, where books are born, I may have wanted to experience that disaster myself.

Questions such as, What would it be like? or What would *I* have done? nagged at me. I wanted to know, and writing Dan's story was the best way I knew to find out.

In one sense, *Night of the Twisters* arrived whole in my mind. The actual storm—where and when it took place, how it progressed—gave me a setting. What happened to my cousin provided a plot framework. Newspaper accounts offered one great story after another.

In another way, *Night of the Twisters* arrived in bits and pieces—as a mountain of details that I must make into fiction. Compare writing a novel to finding a box of bicycle parts on the doorstep. Your heart sinks peering in at the jumble of spokes, chain links, rims, brakes, and handlebars, knowing you'll have to assemble everything (without a how-to manual).

In writing about the Grand Island Disaster, there were a daunting number of bits and pieces to think about. The problem was to arrange, fit, and adjust all those parts to make the book "run" as smoothly and perfectly as a new bike.

For once, deciding on a title was easy. The one I chose would do three jobs for me. It would hook the reader, set time limits for the story, and create a mood. Take the word *night,* for instance. Forget peaceful sleep! How about a night of terror and flight? How about a single night that tests a character's courage and changes everything, even what that person values? Notice, too, the *s* at the end of the word *twisters.* Dan would survive no ordinary summer storm.

"*Multiple* tornadoes," said the news reports.

I wrote the opening in order to meet Dan Hatch, so I could begin to know him. Research came next. I made many trips to the library, where I studied weather books and newspapers, taking notes. I pored over news photos with a magnifying glass and pestered my cousin with questions: "Exactly what were you thinking when the house exploded overhead?"

The book was only half-finished when I knew I had to visit Grand Island. I wanted to talk to survivors. I needed to see South Locust and Meves Bowl, places I was writing about. I hoped to experience again the sounds and smells, the *feel* of a Nebraska spring.

I spent two stormy weeks interviewing in Grand Island and Hastings. A civil defense chief, a meteorologist, police officers, journalists all talked to me. Everyone remembered the night of June 3, 1980 in vivid detail. In the end, my best interviews were with elementary school students who had lost their homes. They knew first-hand how it would be for Dan and Arthur and were able to communicate their feelings to me.

Time spent day-dreaming (a form of planning) may be as important to me as the time actually spent writing a book. Can you imagine *working* while walking or swimming, staring off into the distance, or scrubbing floors? Eventually, though, I had to get on with the BIG JOB—

putting words and sentences down on the page to create a story.

Including research, *Night of the Twisters* took most of a year to write. I went over each chapter seven to twelve times, then revised again after my editor read the manuscript.

The book begins slowly, then "winds up," as we imagine a twister would. Once the reader knows and cares about the characters, the first tornado strikes. From that point on, the pace never lets up.

My reward comes when someone writes to say, "Dan Hatch was a boy just like me." Then I know the reader and I have grabbed hands. We've come through a life-threatening disaster together and are somehow better for it.

I hope we'll meet again. Maybe in the pages of another book.

THINKING ABOUT IT

 1 Dan is scared when the tornado comes, but he acts bravely. What have you done even though you were scared?

2 Dan and Arthur knew what to do in a tornado. What warnings told them it was time to take action? What steps did they take to protect themselves?

3 What do you think Dan and his family will do to get their lives back to normal?

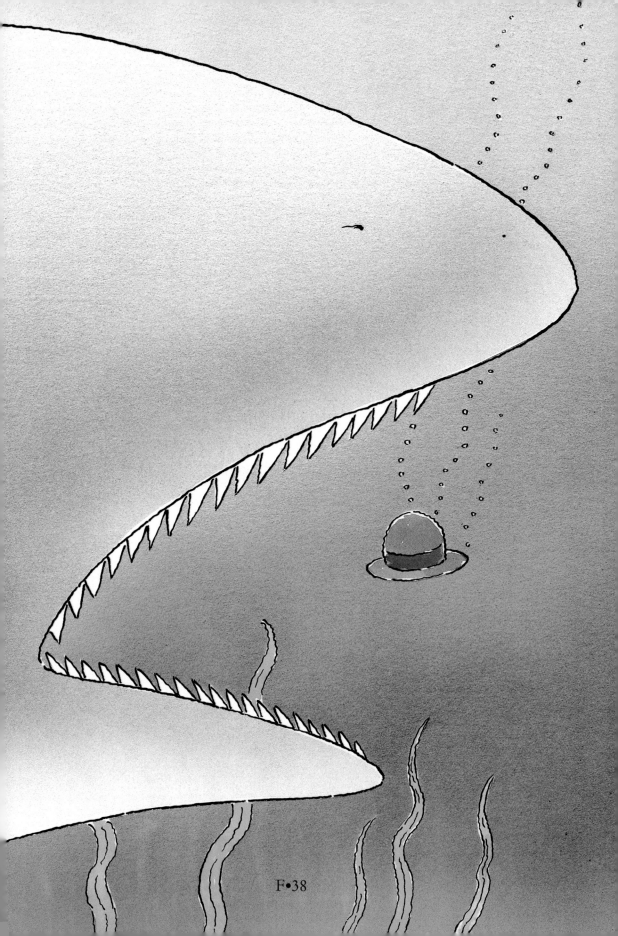

F•38

About the teeth of sharks

by john ciardi

The thing about a shark is—teeth,
One row above, one row beneath.

Now take a close look. Do you find
It has another row behind?

Still closer—here, I'll hold your hat:
Has it a third row behind that?

Now look in and . . . Look out! Oh my,
I'll *never* know now! Well, goodbye.

COURAGE

by Emily Hearn

Courage is when you're
allergic to cats and

your new friend says can
you come to her house to
play after school and

stay to dinner then
maybe go skating and
sleep overnight? And,

she adds, you can pet
her small kittens! Oh,
how you ache to. It

takes courage to
say "no" to all that.

In the Dark of Night

by *Aileen Fisher*

A mouse goes out
in the dark of night
without a lantern
or other light.
She's not afraid
of the dark at all,
though the night's so big
and herself so small.

A Leak in the Dike

by Paul T. Nolan

CHARACTERS

GRANDFATHER
GRANDDAUGHTER
JAN VAN HOOF, *the hero of Haarlem*
NETTY
VINCENT
JULIANA
ADRIAN HAAS, *the bovenmeester (schoolmaster)*
BOREIN APELDOORN

TIME: *Late afternoon.*
SETTING: *The base of the dike in Haarlem, bordered with tulips.*
AT RISE: GRANDFATHER *and* GRANDDAUGHTER *enter from left. The little girl is skipping and singing.*

GRANDDAUGHTER *(Singing to tune of "Yankee Doodle")*:

> *Yanker didee, dudel down*
>
> *Didee dudel lawnter*
>
> *Yanker viver, voyer vown,*
>
> *Botwemelk und Tawnter.*

(She stops as she sees the tulips, and runs to them.)
Look, Grandfather, tulips. Aren't they pretty?

GRANDFATHER: The prettiest in the world, my child.

GRANDDAUGHTER: See how straight they stand.

GRANDFATHER: Everything Dutch stands straight, my child. And our tulips should do no less.

GRANDDAUGHTER: Don't all tulips stand straight, Grandfather? Even English tulips and French tulips?

GRANDFATHER: Yes, but that's because all the tulips of the world first came from Holland. But even so, they don't stand so straight in other lands as here.

GRANDDAUGHTER: Is that really true, Grandfather?

GRANDFATHER *(Laughs.)*: I like to think it is true. Every year when we ship our tulips all over the world, I like to think they droop a little in other lands because they are homesick for the Dutch soil.

GRANDDAUGHTER: Grandfather, you are fooling me. I don't think flowers even know what soil they are on.

GRANDFATHER *(bending over and picking up a handful of earth)*: Everything that ever lived or grew in Holland knows Dutch soil. It's a special kind of earth. It was won with a special kind of work and love.

GRANDDAUGHTER: You mean because we took it from the sea, Grandfather?

GRANDFATHER: Because we took it, and because we hold it. *(He pats the side of the dike.)* We and our good dikes.

GRANDDAUGHTER: You love these old dikes, don't you, Grandfather?

GRANDFATHER: Like a bird loves his wings. And for the same reason: they keep us free.

GRANDDAUGHTER: Tell me again about the time the dike broke, Grandfather.

GRANDFATHER: I have told you a thousand times, but all right. Somewhere a little leak started, and the sea seeped in, then the leak became a hole, then the hole became a gateway. And the sea rushed in. And soon our land was covered.

GRANDDAUGHTER: All from just a little leak, Grandfather?

GRANDFATHER: All from just a little leak. It's like a little hole in a balloon, and the sea is like the air in the balloon. But come. Your mother is waiting for us, and if we are late for our supper, she will not let us go walking tomorrow.

GRANDDAUGHTER: All right, Grandfather. *(She starts skipping and singing. "Yanker didee, dudel down," and exits.)*

GRANDFATHER *(patting the dike)*: Old Friend, stand guard and keep the North Sea out of our beds tonight. *(Exits after GRANDDAUGHTER. JAN and NETTY enter from left. He carries a book which he is reading. She carries a basket, covered with a white napkin.)*

NETTY *(Sees the tulips and rushes to them.)*: Look, Jan, the tulips are in bloom.

JAN *(without looking up)*: Of course. Tulips are always in bloom in April.

NETTY: You must have read that in your book, for you never take your head out of it to look at anything.

JAN *(looking up)*: Are you angry with me, Netty?

NETTY: No, I am not angry with you, Jan van Hoof, but it is not very pleasant to walk along with a person with his head in a book all the time.

JAN: I am sorry, Netty. I did not think. But books have such wonderful things in them, that every time I see a new book it is like seeing a window that looks into a land one has never visited.

NETTY: There are many wonderful things outside books too, you know.

JAN: That's true, but they are even more wonderful after you see them in a book. Take this old dike, for example. You can just look at it, and all you can see is a stone wall. But then you read about it, and you see the thousands of people who have worked for hundreds of years to build it and keep it in repair. And you see the sea beyond the wall, and you see the days of the past—bad days when the sea broke through the wall. And good days when the dikes were rebuilt. And it all becomes much more exciting.

NETTY: But you don't see the dike that is here, just the one in the book. You don't look at life—just at books.

JAN: I see the dike here! See, I am looking at it!

NETTY: You don't even see what is right beneath your nose. Look, there is a little leak, and you didn't even see it.

JAN *(excited)*: What? Where? It can't be. Do not joke about such things.

NETTY: I am not joking. There is a leak! Right here. *(She points to a place in the dike near the ground.)* You see! All the time you tell me about how wonderful the dikes of Holland are, and here right in front of you there is one with a leak, and you did not even see it.

JAN *(looking at leak)*: We have to find something to stop this leak, Netty.

NETTY: It is only a little leak. It can do no harm.

JAN: It is only a little leak now. In an hour it will be a hole. In two hours it will be a river.

NETTY: From such a little trickle? I don't believe it. Why, the hole is so small, you could plug it with your finger.

JAN *(looking closely, and putting his finger in the hole in the dike)*: Yes, it just fits. But it is cold. Netty, run quickly and bring someone to fix the hole. I will hold my finger here until you return.

NETTY: I don't know if I can. I must take this food to Aunt Mecka in Haarlem. She is ill, and there is no one to care for her.

JAN: You can take the food later. This is important, Netty.

NETTY: I am already late now, and if I do not hurry, it will be dark before I get there.

JAN: It doesn't matter. You must find someone to come and fix the leak.

NETTY: It does too matter! My mother would not like me to be out alone after dark.

JAN: Netty, listen to me. This is serious. If this leak is not stopped, the whole city may awaken tomorrow and find itself under the sea.

NETTY: Well—I don't know. *Somebody* else will come. My mother would never let me go to my aunt's again if I did not get there by dark.

JAN: She will understand.

NETTY: She will understand that I didn't get there.

JAN: Please, Netty, you must get someone.

NETTY: Well, I'll try. But if I don't come back, you'll know I didn't see anyone. *(She exits right, running.)*

JAN *(yelling after her)*: You have to see someone! Hurry, I can feel the water around my finger. *(He sits down and tries to get comfortable, holding his finger in the dike all the while.)* Oh, this water is cold, and I think my finger is swelling. All the better to plug the leak, I guess. *(The stage lights begin to dim very slowly.)* What if Netty doesn't find anyone? What can I do? *(He sits quietly for a few seconds, and then he starts to sing quietly and rather tunelessly.)* "Yanker didee, dudel down, Didee dudel lawnter . . ." The leak seems to be getting larger. *(Yells.)* Help! Help! Somebody come. The dike has a leak. Help! Help! *(He waits a moment.)* I'd better save my strength. I must stay awake. I'll sing some more. *"Yanker didee, dudel down . . ."* Won't somebody come? Please, somebody, come! *(The curtain falls or the lights go out, to indicate the passage of time. When the scene is revealed again, the stage is in moonlight, and* JAN *appears to be asleep, leaning against the dike. He straightens up suddenly.)* Have I been asleep? The leak! It seems larger, but no water is coming through. Where is Netty? Why doesn't she come? It is so cold here. I wish that I had worn more clothes. *(He awkwardly tries to get more comfortable.)* I am stiff all over, and my finger aches like a toothache. Maybe I could take my finger out and run and get help before anything happens. No, I'd better not try. Anyway, my finger is so swollen that it probably wouldn't come out easily. *(Yells.)* Help! Help! Doesn't anyone hear me? Doesn't anyone hear me? (VINCENT *and* JULIANA *come creeping in, holding hands, and looking frightened.)*

VINCENT: Jan! Jan van Hoof, are you here?

JULIANA: He's not here! I told you he wouldn't be. That Netty is always making things up. He is home asleep.

JAN: Help! Help! Over here!

VINCENT: There he is. Over there. *(They run to him.)*

JAN: Why did you take so long to come? My legs are so stiff from the cold, I shall not be able to walk. Have you brought someone to fix the leak?

VINCENT: We would have come sooner—

JULIANA: But at first we did not believe Netty.

VINCENT: And then we were afraid to tell anyone, for fear that if Netty were making a joke, she would get into trouble. And then we had to wait until everyone went to sleep so that we could sneak out. Is there really a leak, Jan?

JAN: Yes, here. See—I have my finger in it. I think it is getting a little larger, but it is all right now that you are here.

JULIANA: What should we do?

JAN: Go and bring someone to fix the leak. And do it quickly.

VINCENT: Whom should we bring? I would not want to wake my father.

JAN: Just bring anyone: Van Deiper, the gate-keeper, or Bovenmeester Haas, or your uncle, or anyone. But please hurry. I ache and I am cold all over, and the sea is pushing against this hole so that I am not sure how much longer my finger can hold the water back.

VINCENT: I shall go right away.

JULIANA: Wait a minute, Vincent. We *can't* go now.

VINCENT: Why not?

JULIANA: How will we explain that we have sneaked out of our beds at four o'clock in the morning?

VINCENT: I hadn't thought of that.

JULIANA: You know what Mother and Father would say.

JAN: Listen to me, both of you. There is no time to worry about what may happen to us. If help does not come soon, the whole dike may crack and the North Sea come in.

JULIANA: Well, I guess you're right, but I just know we are going to get into trouble.

VINCENT: Can't you wait just a little longer, Jan? It will be morning soon, and then we can bring help.

JAN: I can wait if I have to. But will the North Sea wait? Look, already a few drops are starting to get past my finger.

JULIANA (*bending over and looking closely*): It is starting to seep in. And your finger looks so strange. Does it hurt, Jan?

JAN: I don't feel anything in it now, but I can't move it. It is just stiff, I guess. But will you please go for help? Even now it may be too late.

JULIANA: Yes, we'll go.

VINCENT: Who will hear us knocking on the door at this hour of the morning?

JULIANA: I will go to Borein Apeldoorn's house. She gets up very early to milk the cows. She is very old and wise, and she will know what to do.

VINCENT: I shall go to the schoolmaster's house. Sometimes Bovenmeester Haas sits up all night looking in his books. He may still be awake.
(VINCENT *runs off right, and* JULIANA *left.*)

JAN: But hurry! Hurry! *(Curtain or blackout. When the scene is revealed again, it is early morning. JAN now has finger in the dike, while his other hand is pressed around the finger to try to hold back the water that is seeping through. GRANDFATHER and GRANDDAUGHTER come in.)*

GRANDDAUGHTER: Grandfather, look at that little boy. What a funny place to sit.

GRANDFATHER: Why, it is young Jan van Hoof. *(going to him)* What are you doing there, boy?

JAN: Thank heavens you've come by. There is a leak in the dike, and I am trying to hold the water back.

GRANDFATHER: A leak in the dike! Good heavens, let me see. *(He bends over and looks.)* Yes. Yes, I see. And there is water coming in. But your finger! What has happened to it?

JAN: I don't know, sir. It's stopped feeling.

GRANDFATHER: Stopped feeling? How long have you been here?

JAN: Since last evening. It's been only one night, but it seems like a whole lifetime ago. *(JULIANA enters, leading BOREIN APELDOORN, who carries a blanket.)*

JULIANA: There he is, Frau Apeldoorn. I told you. I told you. *(running to JAN)* I came as fast as I could, Jan. She was in the barn when I got there, and I did not know it. Hasn't Vincent come back yet?

JAN: No, but it will be all right now. Thank you, Juliana.

GRANDFATHER: First, we have to find something to plug this leak, Jan, and then we will get your finger out.

BOREIN APELDOORN *(going to* JAN*)*: I have brought ointment for his finger and a blanket to wrap him in. The poor boy. All night in this April cold. He'll catch his death. *(VINCENT enters half-running, followed by ADRIAN HAAS, carrying a box.)*

VINCENT *(yelling as he enters)*: Jan! Jan, I'm back. I have the Bovenmeester with me. *(He sees the others.)* Oh! I have kept you waiting too long, but I ran as fast as I could.

JAN: It is all right, Vincent. It is all right. You came in time.

HAAS: I have brought mortar and stone to fix the leak. *(He joins the others at the leak.)* Easy now. Here, ease his finger out gently.

BOREIN APELDOORN: Men! *(takes salve from her pocket)* Here, put this around his finger, and then it will slide out more easily.

HAAS: There, it's coming. There. It's out. *(helps JAN away from the dike)* If you will take care of him, I'll fix this leak. Again a Dutchman has beaten the sea! *(He bends over and works on the dike.)*

GRANDFATHER *(helping* JAN *a few feet from the leak, while* BOREIN APELDOORN *covers his shoulders with a blanket)*: Here, Jan, sit here for a moment, and Borein Apeldoorn will have that finger right in a minute.

BOREIN APELDOORN: You have the biggest finger in all Holland now, Jan.

GRANDFATHER: And the biggest heart!

HAAS: There, it's plugged now. *(standing up and coming to* JAN*)* And how's our hero?

JAN: I'm no hero. I just put my finger in a hole, that's all.

HAAS: You did a good deal more than that. You saved Haarlem from the sea.

GRANDFATHER: Even more than that, Bovenmeester. Jan has proved again that a leak cannot show itself anywhere in Holland, but that a good stout Dutch finger will be there ready to stop it, at any cost. Somebody will one day build a statue for you, Jan, and on it he will write, "To honor the boy who symbolizes the eternal struggle of Holland against the sea."

BOREIN APELDOORN: You men, building monuments with your words! What our hero needs more than statues is his breakfast. I wish I had thought to bring something for him to eat. (NETTY *enters, running and carrying her basket.*)

NETTY: Jan! Jan, are you here?

JAN *(starting to stand)*: Over here, Netty.

NETTY *(coming to him)*: I came as soon as I could, Jan. And I brought you something. *(reaches into her basket)* Breakfast. *(She brings out a covered jug and a piece of pastry.)* Milk and kuchen. (JAN *takes them and eats hungrily.*)

BOREIN APELDOORN: Now there's a Dutch woman for you. She knows enough to feed her hero.

VINCENT: Well, I say three cheers for Jan van Hoof, the hero of Haarlem.

JAN: And I say, have you got another piece of kuchen, Netty? *(All laugh as the curtain falls.)*

THE END

THINKING ABOUT IT

1. When you were through reading *A Leak in the Dike*, what parts of the story stood out in your mind?

2. Why is a tiny, finger-sized hole in the dike such a big problem?

3. Jan saved the town of Haarlem from a flood, so you, the mayor of Haarlem, decide to reward Jan with a gift. What gift do you choose? Why?

READY, SET, DIVE!

by Ann McGovern

Going on a Night Dive

I must be crazy. It's nighttime and here I am on this dive boat, in total darkness. And I'm scared to death.

The sky above me is black except for a half-moon. The sea around me is black. I see lights twinkling on the distant shore. Land seems far away. But land is where most twelve-year-old girls should be. So what am I doing on the sea?

I'm going on a night dive, that's what I'm doing. In just a few minutes, I'll be in that black sea, and it's too late to do anything about it.

How did I get myself into this? By opening up my big mouth, that's how.

Mom and I have been scuba diving on this beautiful Caribbean island for a week now. We've been diving every day. It's been great.

When Jim, who is in charge of diving, first met me, he asked to see my "C" card—my scuba certification card. It proves I've had the proper diving training. You have to be twelve before you can be certified. I went to the local "Y" for my course.

Yesterday Mom told Jim about her work as a marine biologist and about her interest in parrot fishes.

"There are lots of different parrot fishes on our reefs," he said.

Then I blew it. Why don't I think before I speak, like Mom is always telling me to do?

"Really?" I said. "Do you have the kind of parrot fish that spins a cocoon around itself at night?"

Coral reef; parrot fish in foreground

Jim grinned. "Sure, kid," he said. "Since you're such a hotshot diver, how about a night dive to see for yourself?"

So that's why I'm on Jim's boat tonight with Mom and the other divers. About to take a plunge into inky waters. I'll probably never even see a parrot fish sleeping in its cocoon. I'll probably be eaten alive by a shark as soon as I hit the water.

Getting Ready

"Time to suit up," Jim calls. In dive language that means to get ready. On normal day dives, I'm ready before anyone else. But not tonight.

Jim switches on the boat lights. Mom pats my head. I think she knows how scared I am. She's getting into her special dive suit. Most of the other divers wear rubber wet suits too.

It's a warm night and the water will be warm too— about 82 degrees Fahrenheit. On these warm islands, you don't need to cover yourself up for the temperature. Wet suits or shirts and jeans protect you from stinging and scratching coral you might bump into—especially in the dark.

The only thing I don't like about diving is getting ready. There's so much stuff!

You need to wear fins on your feet, so you can move easily without using your arms.

You need a mask so that you can see clearly underwater. You need a snorkel only if you want to swim on top of the water.

You need to wear a weight belt too, with just the right amount of weights on it. The weights help you get down without having to swim hard.

The BC, or *buoyancy compensator*, is very important. It's like a vest and can be filled with air. You can put a little air into the BC and make yourself weightless so you can just float underwater without sinking or rising. If you want to come up, you can put more air into your BC.

The most important equipment is the tank of compressed air on your back. One part of the regulator screws on the tank, and the other part, at the end of the short hose, goes in your mouth. You breathe in and out, nice and easy, as long as you have air in your tank. That's why you need a pressure gauge. It shows how much air you have in your tank. I've always been amazed that a tank is so heavy on land. It weighs more than thirty pounds—but once I'm in the water, I hardly feel it!

Your dive watch shows how long you've been under. And your depth gauge shows how deep you are.

It's a good idea to wear cotton or rubber gloves. You don't want to hold onto strange coral with your bare hands. You may get scratched, and fire coral can sting.

When you go on a night dive, you must carry your own light so you can see what's out there on the reef. Mom has thought of something else, too—light sticks that glow green in the dark. She fastens one to the back of my tank and puts another on her tank. That way, I'll be able to tell where she is at all times. And she'll always know where I am.

Diver and reef fish

Mom is wearing a compass. It's especially important at night to be able to find your way back to the boat.

Jim says having the right equipment is crucial. It makes you feel safer. It makes the whole dive experience easier. You don't have to swim hard or breathe hard or worry about anything not working. Your dive lasts longer when you take it nice and easy and don't get upset.

I look around at the other divers. They don't look at all scared. One couple has been diving for twenty years. Randy has gray hair and a lot of wrinkles. His wife, Sally, has been talking about their new granddaughter. It seems strange to think of grandparents scuba diving!

Then there's Don and his cute girlfriend, Jenny, who is a teacher. Why can't I have a teacher who scuba dives?

There's also Joe, an underwater photographer, who's very busy fussing with his cameras. He's taking a big strobe light down with him. I think I'll stick close to him. I'll need all the extra light I can get. Jim is carrying a big light too.

Jim makes an announcement. "You've all dived with me before so you know the rules. We'll make a backward entry. That's when you sit on the side of the boat and fall over backwards," Jim explains. "It sounds hard, but it's an easy way to get into the water. Stay close together and stay with me. The boat light will be on all the time. And another light hanging from the boat into the water will help guide you back. We'll enter the water and go down the line. We'll meet on the reef, thirty feet below the boat. Then we'll begin exploring the reef. At some point, I'll give a signal by twirling my light. That means you should all turn off your lights for a minute or two."

Turn off our lights! He's got to be out of his mind. It's bad enough having only a tiny little beam of light in that huge black sea. But to be in total darkness? No way. Not me. I won't do it. I'm leaving my light on all the time.

I sit on the side on the boat. Jim helps me on with my tank and turns on my air.

"Let's get wet," he calls.

This is it.

I look out at the smooth black water, gulp, and roll over backward into the night-dark sea.

The First Moments

I'm in the water, but where's Mom? For a moment, I feel panic rising in me. Everywhere is pitch black, except for the narrow beam of my light in front of me.

Something touches me from behind. A shark? I whirl around. It's Mom. I tell myself to calm down. Mom takes my hand and we start down the line.

Is that the noise of my air bubbles or my heart beating like a drum? My light shows up specks in the dark water as we make our way slowly down to the reef. The specks are *plankton*—tiny creatures drifting through the water.

On day dives, I usually get very excited the minute I hit the water. I just love the feeling of being weightless, like an astronaut—a feeling half like a bird and half like a fish as I swim slowly over the reef or stand on my head.

But tonight I feel only fear. I can hardly tell up from down. The stick of glowing light on Mom's tank comforts me a little.

Suddenly pain shoots into my left ear. Nuts. I was so busy being scared that I forgot to relieve the pressure. I let go of Mom's hand, pinch my nose, and blow out. The pressure goes away.

I look up. The light hanging from the boat is a pale green hazy ball. I see the lights of the other divers below me. I aim mine in front of me. Dozens of tiny shrimplike creatures dance in the beam of the light, like moths around a candle. They are *larvae*, babies of sea

animals. When I move my light, they go away. When I keep the light still, they come back.

My fins touch the sandy bottom. It takes only one minute to go down thirty feet but it feels like ten minutes.

I count lights. There are eight of us, including Jim. Jim said we would be able to see the moonlight. He was right. It shimmers on the surface of the water like a pool of light.

A strange long tail stretches out on the sandy bottom from under a coral head. The "tiger tail" is a member of the sea cucumber family. Sea cucumbers feed on bits of food and tiny plants called *algae*. I keep my light on it. It begins to shorten, like a huge rubber band.

There are spiny sea urchins everywhere! By day they hide in the coral without moving. I have to be very careful not to step on one. Their sharp spines can jab right through the fins. Tonight, the spiny sea urchins are walking around like pin cushions on invisible feet. They browse on algae. The mouth of a spiny sea urchin is underneath its body. I shine my light on them. In between their black spines, I can see their red and blue bodies.

There's an arrow crab. The arrow crab is just one of hundreds of different kinds of crabs on the reef. It has a pointy head like an arrow and long thin legs like a spider. By day it's a shy creature. But at night it's right out in the open.

Cup coral polyps

And so many brittle stars swarm over the sponges. Each of their five arms moves like a snake and is covered with bristles. They scurry away under the beam of my light. Brittle stars live in sponges by day. At night they creep out to feed. If you catch a brittle star by one of its arms, the arm will break off. But it will soon grow a new one.

On a wall are bright orange cup corals, looking like flowers. The stony coral heads have turned soft and fuzzy.

Hard stony coral is made up of millions of tiny, soft animals that build limestone walls around themselves.

The soft animals are called *polyps*. By day, you can usually see only the hard walls. But at night, the little polyps reach out to feed, covering the hard coral with a blanket of soft fuzz. If you look closely, you will see that each bit of fuzz has six little waving arms, called *tentacles*. At night the tentacles reach out to catch plankton. The soft corals of the reef, such as the sea fans and sea whips, have eight tentacles. They feed by day as well as by night.

I start to move away from the circle of lights. Mom pulls me back. Jim has begun his signal. He is twirling his light around and around.

One by one, the divers turn their lights off. I guess I have to now. My heart pounds as I turn off my light.

Now there is nothing but dark. Then little by little I begin to see the shapes of the divers. I move my arm. A stream of tiny stars trails from my fingertips.

Jim begins to swim around us. As he swims, pinpoints of light scatter around his body. The lights are made by a variety of tiny creatures. When they are disturbed, they glow like sparklers and fireflies. There are millions of these creatures in the warm waters of the coral reef. Their glow is called *bioluminescence*, which means "living light."

Night diving. It's still spooky, still scary. But I must admit, it's beginning to be kind of magical too.

THINKING ABOUT IT

1. Jim the diver invites you on a night dive. Will you go? Why or why not?

2. What equipment do you need for a night dive? What is the purpose of each piece of equipment?

3. Spiny sea urchins, arrow crabs, cup coral—the divers encounter these and other sea creatures. Now they come upon a creature not mentioned in the selection. What is it? What happens?

Another Book by Ann McGovern

For more diving excitement, read *Down Under, Down Under* about diving on Australia's Great Barrier Reef.

> *Jackie Robinson was more than just my teammate. He had a tremendous amount of talent, ability, and dedication. Jackie set a standard for future generations of ballplayers. He was a winner. Jackie Robinson was also a* man.

PEE WEE REESE
OCTOBER 31, 1989

TEAMMATES

by Peter Golenbock

Once upon a time in America, when automobiles were black and looked like tanks and laundry was white and hung on clotheslines to dry, there were two wonderful baseball leagues that no longer exist. They were called the Negro Leagues.

The Negro Leagues had extraordinary players, and adoring fans came to see them wherever they played. They were heroes, but players in the Negro Leagues didn't make much money and their lives on the road were hard.

Laws against segregation didn't exist in the 1940s. In many places in this country, African Americans were not allowed to go to the same schools and churches as white people. They couldn't sit in the front of a bus or trolley car. They couldn't drink from the same drinking fountains that white people drank from.

Back then, many hotels didn't rent rooms to black people, so the Negro League players slept in their cars. Many towns had no restaurants that would

Ebbets Field was a neighborhood ballpark where fans from all over Brooklyn came to
witness baseball's "great experiment."

serve them, so they often had to eat meals that they could buy and carry with them.

Life was very different for the players in the Major Leagues. They were the leagues for white players. Compared to the Negro League players, white players were very well paid. They stayed in good hotels and ate in fine restaurants. Their pictures were put on baseball cards and the best players became famous all over the world.

Many Americans knew that racial prejudice was wrong, but few dared to challenge openly the way things were. And many people were apathetic about racial problems. Some feared that it could be dangerous to object. Vigilante groups, like the Ku Klux Klan, reacted violently against those who tried to change the way African Americans were treated.

The general manager of the Brooklyn Dodgers baseball team was a man by the name of Branch Rickey. He was not afraid of change. He wanted to treat the Dodger fans to the best players he could find, regardless of the color of their skin. He thought segregation was unfair and wanted to give everyone, regardless of race or creed, an opportunity to compete equally on ballfields across America.

To do this, the Dodgers needed one special man.

Branch Rickey launched a search for him. He was looking for a star player in the Negro Leagues who would be able to compete successfully despite threats on his life or attempts to injure him. He would have to possess the self-control not to fight back when opposing players tried to intimidate or hurt him.

If this man disgraced himself on the field, Rickey knew, his opponents would use it as an excuse to keep blacks out of Major League baseball for many more years.

Rickey thought Jackie Robinson might be just the man.

Jackie rode the train to Brooklyn to meet Mr. Rickey. When Mr. Rickey told him, "I want a man with the courage not to fight back," Jackie Robinson replied, "If you take this gamble, I will do my best to perform." They shook hands. Branch Rickey and Jackie Robinson were starting on what would be known in history as "the great experiment."

At spring training with the Dodgers, Jackie was mobbed by African Americans, young and old, as if he were a savior. He was the first black player to try out for a Major League team. If he succeeded, they knew, others would follow.

Initially, life with the Dodgers was for Jackie a series of humiliations. The players on his team who came from the South, men who had been taught to avoid African Americans since childhood, moved to another table whenever he sat down next to them. Many opposing players were cruel to him, calling him nasty names from their dugouts. A few tried to hurt him with their spiked shoes. Pitchers aimed at his head. And he received threats on his life, both from individuals and from organizations like the Ku Klux Klan.

Despite all the difficulties, Jackie Robinson didn't give up. He made the Brooklyn Dodgers team.

But making the Dodgers was only the beginning. Jackie had to face abuse and hostility throughout the season, from April through September. His worst pain was inside. Often he felt very alone. On the road he had to live by himself, because only the white players were allowed in the hotels in towns where the team played.

The whole time Pee Wee Reese, the Dodger shortstop, was growing up in Louisville, Kentucky, he had rarely even seen an African American, unless it was in the back of a bus. Most of his friends and relatives hated the idea of his playing on the same field as a black man. In addition, Pee Wee Reese had more to lose than the other players when Jackie joined the team.

Jackie had been a shortstop, and everyone thought that Jackie would take Pee Wee's job. Lesser men might have felt anger toward Jackie, but Pee Wee was different. He told himself, "If he's good enough to take my job, he deserves it."

When his Southern teammates circulated a petition to throw Jackie off the team and asked him to sign it, Pee Wee responded, "I don't care if this man is black, blue, or striped"—and refused to sign. "He can play and he can help us win," he told the others. "That's what counts."

Very early in the season, the Dodgers traveled west to Ohio to play the Cincinnati Reds. Cincinnati is near Pee Wee's hometown of Louisville.

Pee Wee Reese and Jackie Robinson showed qualities of tolerance and courage that made them Hall of Fame ballplayers and champion human beings.

The Reds played in a small ballpark where the fans sat close to the field. The players could almost feel the breath of the fans on the backs of their necks. Many who came that day screamed terrible, hateful things at Jackie when the Dodgers were on the field.

More than anything else, Pee Wee Reese believed in doing what was right. When he heard the fans yelling at Jackie, Pee Wee decided to take a stand.

With his head high, Pee Wee walked directly from his shortstop position to where Jackie was playing first base. The taunts and shouting of the fans were ringing in Pee Wee's ears. It saddened him, because he knew it could have been his friends and neighbors. Pee Wee's legs felt heavy, but he knew what he had to do.

As he walked toward Jackie wearing the gray Dodger uniform, he looked into his teammate's bold, pained eyes. The first baseman had done nothing to provoke the hostility except that he sought to be treated as an equal. Jackie was grim with anger. Pee Wee smiled broadly as he reached Jackie. Jackie smiled back.

Stopping beside Jackie, Pee Wee put his arm around Jackie's shoulders. An audible gasp rose up from the crowd when they saw what Pee Wee had done. Then there was silence.

Outlined on a sea of green grass stood these two great athletes, one black, one white, both wearing the same team uniform.

"I am standing by him," Pee Wee Reese said to the world. "This man is my teammate."

TEAMMATES STICK TOGETHER

by Peter Golenbock

When I was doing research for my book *Bums*, a history of the Brooklyn Dodgers, one of the team's pitchers, Rex Barney, sat and told me the story of Pee Wee Reese's courageous stand on behalf of Jackie Robinson. This is the story of *Teammates*.

Pee Wee Reese was a southerner and he was famous as a ballplayer. By standing up for Robinson, Reese faced the possibility of stinging criticism from friends, family, and the other players in the major leagues. But Pee Wee Reese believed everyone should get a

fair chance, regardless of skin color. By supporting Robinson, Reese set a good example for all players in the league.

Jackie Robinson joined the Brooklyn Dodgers in 1947. He quickly established himself as the most exciting player in the major leagues. He hit .297 and led the National League with twenty-nine stolen bases. He was named the National League Rookie of the Year. He led the Dodgers to the National League pennant.

Robinson, who became a lasting symbol of African American pride and accomplishment, never made a big deal out of Reese's support of him. And to Pee Wee Reese, his action was nothing out of the ordinary.

But for me, and for the many fans who loved Jackie Robinson and Pee Wee Reese and the Brooklyn Dodgers, the two men were great Americans who deserve their place in history.

THINKING ABOUT IT

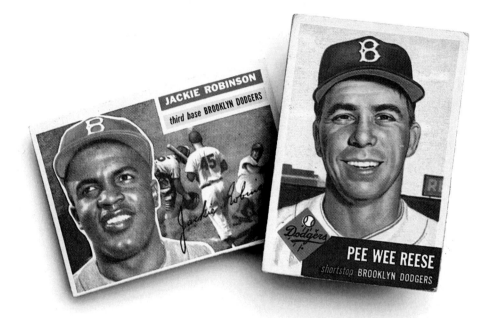

1 Imagine that you could have met Jackie Robinson during his first season with the Brooklyn Dodgers. What would you have said to him?

2 "Jackie Robinson and Pee Wee Reese were heroes." Do you agree? Support your opinion with evidence from the selection.

3 You are in the stands at the game between the Cincinnati Reds and the Brooklyn Dodgers. You want to show your support for Jackie Robinson. How will you do it?

F•86

NADIA THE WILLFUL

by Sue Alexander

illustrations by Lloyd Bloom

IN THE LAND OF THE DRIFTING SANDS where the Bedouin move their tents to follow the fertile grasses, there lived a girl whose stubbornness and flashing temper caused her to be known throughout the desert as Nadia the Willful.

Nadia's father, the sheik Tarik, whose kindness and graciousness caused his name to be praised in every tent, did not know what to do with his willful daughter.

Only Hamed, the eldest of Nadia's six brothers and Tarik's favorite son, could calm Nadia's temper when it flashed. "Oh, angry one," he would say, "shall we see how long you can stay that way?" And he would laugh and tease and pull at her dark hair until she laughed back. Then she would follow Hamed wherever he led.

One day before dawn, Hamed mounted his father's great white stallion and rode to the west to seek new grazing ground for the sheep. Nadia stood with her father at the edge of the oasis and watched him go.

Hamed did not return.

Nadia rode behind her father as he traveled across the desert from oasis to oasis, seeking Hamed.

Shepherds told them of seeing a great white stallion fleeing before the pillars of wind that stirred the sand. And they said that the horse carried no rider.

Passing merchants, their camels laden with spices and sweets for the bazaar, told of the emptiness of the desert they had crossed.

Tribesmen, strangers, everyone whom Tarik asked, sighed and gazed into the desert, saying, "Such is the will of Allah."

At last Tarik knew in his heart that his favorite son, Hamed, had been claimed, as other Bedouin before him, by the drifting sands. And he told Nadia what he knew—that Hamed was dead.

Nadia screamed and wept and stamped the sand, crying, "Not even Allah will take Hamed from me!" until her father could bear no more and sternly bade her to silence.

Nadia's grief knew no bounds. She walked blindly through the oasis neither seeing nor hearing those who would console her. And Tarik was silent. For days he sat inside his tent, speaking not at all and barely tasting the meals set before him.

Then, on the seventh day, Tarik came out of his tent. He called all his people to him, and when they were assembled, he spoke. "From this day forward," he said, "let no one utter Hamed's name. Punishment shall be swift for those who would remind me of what I have lost."

Hamed's mother wept at the decree. The people of the clan looked at one another uneasily. All could see the hardness that had settled on the sheik's face and the coldness in his eyes, and so they said nothing. But they obeyed.

Nadia, too, did as her father decreed, though each day held something to remind her of Hamed. As she passed her brothers at play she remembered games Hamed had taught her. As she walked by the women weaving patches for the tents, and heard them talking and laughing, she remembered tales Hamed had told her and how they had made her laugh. And as she watched the shepherds with their flock she remembered the little black lamb Hamed had loved.

F•91

Each memory brought Hamed's name to Nadia's lips, but she stilled the sound. And each time that she did so, her unhappiness grew until, finally, she could no longer contain it. She wept and raged at anyone and anything that crossed her path. Soon everyone at the oasis fled at her approach. And she was more lonely than she had ever been before.

One day, as Nadia passed the place where her brothers were playing, she stopped to watch them. They were playing one of the games that Hamed had taught her. But they were playing it wrong.

Without thinking, Nadia called out to them. "That is not the way! Hamed said that first you jump this way and then you jump back!"

Her brothers stopped their game and looked around in fear. Had Tarik heard Nadia say Hamed's name? But the sheik was nowhere to be seen.

"Teach us, Nadia, as our brother taught you," said her smallest brother.

And so she did. Then she told them of other games and how Hamed had taught her to play them. And as she spoke of Hamed she felt an easing of the hurt within her.

So she went on speaking of him.

She went to where the women sat at their loom and spoke of Hamed. She told them tales that Hamed had told her. And she told how he had made her laugh as he was telling them.

At first the women were afraid to listen to the willful girl and covered their ears, but after a time, they listened and laughed with her.

"Remember your father's promise of punishment!" Nadia's mother warned when she heard Nadia speaking of Hamed. "Cease, I implore you!"

Nadia knew that her mother had reason to be afraid, for Tarik, in his grief and bitterness, had grown quick-tempered and sharp of tongue. But she did not know how to tell her mother that speaking of Hamed eased the pain she felt, and so she said only, "I will speak of my brother! I will!" And she ran away from the sound of her mother's voice.

She went to where the shepherds tended the flock and spoke of Hamed. The shepherds ran from her in fear and hid behind the sheep. But Nadia went on speaking. She told of Hamed's love for the little black lamb and how he had taught it to leap at his whistle. Soon the shepherds left off their hiding and came to listen. Then they told their own stories of Hamed and the little black lamb.

The more Nadia spoke of Hamed, the clearer his face became in her mind. She could see his smile and the light in his eyes. She could hear his voice. And the clearer Hamed's voice and face became, the less Nadia hurt inside and the less her temper flashed. At last, she was filled with peace.

But her mother was still afraid for her willful daughter. Again and again she sought to quiet Nadia so that Tarik's bitterness would not be turned against her. And again and again Nadia tossed her head and went on speaking of Hamed.

Soon, all who listened could see Hamed's face clearly before them.

One day, the youngest shepherd came to Nadia's tent calling, "Come, Nadia! See Hamed's black lamb, it has grown so big and strong!"

But it was not Nadia who came out of the tent.

It was Tarik.

On the sheik's face was a look more fierce than that of a desert hawk, and when he spoke, his words were as sharp as a scimitar.

"I have forbidden my son's name to be said. And I promised punishment to whoever disobeyed my command. So shall it be. Before the sun sets and the moon casts its first shadow on the sand, you will be gone from this oasis—never to return."

"No!" cried Nadia, hearing her father's words.

"I have spoken!" roared the sheik. "It shall be done!"

Trembling, the shepherd went to gather his possessions.

F•97

And the rest of the clan looked at one another uneasily and muttered among themselves.

In the hours that followed, fear of being banished to the desert made everyone turn away from Nadia as she tried to tell them of Hamed and the things he had done and said.

And the less she was listened to, the less she was able to recall Hamed's face and voice. And the less she recalled, the more her temper raged within her, destroying the peace she had found.

By evening, she could stand it no longer. She went to where her father sat, staring into the desert, and stood before him.

"You will not rob me of my brother Hamed!" she cried, stamping her foot. "I will not let you!"

Tarik looked at her, his eyes colder than the desert night.

But before he could utter a word, Nadia spoke again. "Can you recall Hamed's face? Can you still hear his voice?"

Tarik started in surprise, and his answer seemed to come unbidden to his lips. "No, I cannot! Day after day I have sat in this spot where I last saw Hamed, trying to remember the look, the sound, the happiness that was my beloved son—but I cannot."

And he wept.

Nadia's tone became gentle. "There is a way, honored father," she said. "Listen."

F•99

And she began to speak of Hamed. She told of walks she and Hamed had taken, and of talks they had had. She told how he had taught her games, told her tales and calmed her when she was angry. She told many things that she remembered, some happy and some sad.

And when she was done with the telling, she said gently, "Can you not recall him now, Father? Can you not see his face? Can you not hear his voice?"

Tarik nodded through his tears, and for the first time since Hamed had been gone, he smiled.

"Now you see," Nadia said, her tone more gentle than the softest of the desert breezes, "there is a way that Hamed can be with us still."

The sheik pondered what Nadia had said. After a long time, he spoke, and the sharpness was gone from his voice.

"Tell my people to come before me, Nadia," he said. "I have something to say to them."

When all were assembled, Tarik said, "From this day forward, let my daughter Nadia be known not as Willful, but as Wise. And let her name be praised in every tent, for she has given me back my beloved son."

And so it was. The shepherd returned to his flock, kindness and graciousness returned to the oasis, and Nadia's name was praised in every tent. And Hamed lived again—in the hearts of all who remembered him.

F•101

F•102

ABOUT

NADIA THE WILLFUL

by Sue Alexander

NADIA THE WILLFUL came to be written because I was very unhappy. My brother had died, and in their grief neither my father nor my eldest son would talk about him or let me do so in their hearing. I wanted to talk about my brother and the things he had done and said. I was afraid that if he wasn't talked about, he would soon be forgotten. But I didn't know how to say that to my father or my son.

So I decided to write a story in which someone died and was talked about—and therefore remembered. In a story I could say what I hadn't been able to say to my father and my son in real life.

I knew it would be a hard story for me to write. Somehow I would have to achieve some distance from it, not distance in terms of space, but distance from my feelings. Otherwise the result wouldn't be a *story,* but just an outpouring of my feelings. As I thought about the story I wanted to write, it occurred to me that setting the story in another country, in another culture, might be the way to attain the emotional distance that I needed.

It was then that I remembered the Bedouins. When I was in the fifth grade, my parents took me to see a musical stage play about a group of Bedouins. How different they were from people I knew! I was fascinated and wanted to know more about them. So most of my pleasure reading time that year was spent reading every book I could find in the library about Bedouins.

Off to the library I went to read about Bedouins once again. Over a period of several months I read everything I could find—fiction and nonfiction—about Bedouins and the desert where they lived. There

was, it seemed to me as I read, a folk-tale rhythm to the Bedouin way of life. That would be the right rhythm, I decided, for the story I wanted to tell.

Then I began to write. The first paragraph was the hardest; I rewrote it at least fifty times until I found the right words for it. And I didn't find them until after the rest of the story was written—about two months from the day I began it.

My father and my son read the story for the first time after the book was published, and it was only then that they began to be able to talk about my brother. Their grief was finally being eased— as mine had been in the writing of *Nadia the Willful.*

Sue Alexander

THINKING ABOUT IT

1 If you could be a character in this story, which character would you choose? Why?

2 You are Nadia. Help a friend who has just lost her brother. Tell your friend about things you did that made you feel better when your brother, Hamed, died.

3 You can change this story any way you want to. What would you change, or would you leave it just as it is? Why?

Another Book by Sue Alexander

Meet another wise young character in *Lila on the Landing*. What can you do when the other kids in the neighborhood say you are too clumsy to play with them? Lila finds plenty to keep her busy on the landing of her apartment house, and soon the other kids are interested too.

ATARIBA & NIGUAYONA

Adapted by/Adaptado por
Harriet Rohmer & Jesús Guerrero Rea

Little Atariba, with her long black hair and eyes like seashells, was very sick. She lay in a hammock in the hut of the bohique, the village healer. But the bohique could not cure her.

La pequeña Atariba, con su cabello largo y negro y sus ojos como conchas marinas, estaba muy enferma. Yacía en una hamaca en la casucha del bohique, el curandero del pueblo. Pero el bohique no podía curarla.

Atariba—Ah•tah•rée•ba
Niguayona—Nee•gwa•yóh•na
bohique—bo•ée•kay: healer / curandero

Her best friend, Niguayona, watched her sadly. He remembered how happy he had been, wandering with Atariba by the riverbank. Together they had played with the parrots and the furry jutías. Only days before he had made her a beautiful necklace of seashells and green stones.

Time passed and Atariba still did not recover. Niguayona wandered alone along the riverbank, playing his conch-shell horn. "How can Atariba be cured?" he wondered.

One afternoon, a golden-green macaw alighted on Niguayona's shoulder.

"On the far side of the forest grows a tall caimoní tree," said the bird. "Pick the fruit of this tree, place it on the lips of your Atariba, and she will be cured." And having spoken, the golden-green macaw flew off into the forest.

Su mejor amigo, Niguayona, la miraba con tristeza. Recordaba qué contento había estado caminando con Atariba por la orilla del río. Juntos habían jugado con los pericos y las peludas jutías. Apenas unos días antes, él le había fabricado un hermoso collar de conchas y piedritas verdes.

Pasaba el tiempo y Atariba no mejoraba. Niguayona andaba solo por la orilla del río, tocando música en su trompeta de caracol.—¿Qué se podrá hacer para curar a Atariba?—se preguntó.

Una tarde, un papagayo verdidorado vino a parar sobre el hombro de Niguayona. —En la parte más lejana del bosque crece el alto caimoní—dijo el papagayo. Recoge la fruta de ese árbol, ponla sobre los labios de Atariba, y así se curará. Al terminar de hablar, el papagayo verdidorado se echó a volar hacia el bosque.

jutía—hoo•té•ah; small furry animal / animalito de pelaje suave

caimoní—kai•mo•née

Niguayona ran toward the village. After hearing his story, his mother and father agreed that he must try to find the tall caimoni tree. The bohique began to pray for him.

Niguayona entered the forest alone, but he was not afraid. The tree frogs sang to him. An owl called out. Night came quickly and it was soon quite dark. He sat down to rest beneath a large tree and ate a small piece of the cassava cake his mother had given him. Then he said a prayer to Yucaju, the great god of the Taino people.

"Yucaju, dweller of heaven, grant that I may soon find the tall caimoni tree!"

Niguayona corrió hacia el pueblo. Después de haber escuchado su historia, su madre y su padre estuvieron de acuerdo en que tenía que ir en busca del alto caimoní. El bohique comenzó a rezar por él.

Niguayona entró solito al bosque, pero no tenía miedo. Las ranitas arbóreas le cantaban. Una lechuza chilló. La noche llegó rápidamente, y pronto todo estaba oscuro. Niguayona se sentó a descansar debajo de un árbol grande, y comió un pequeño trozo de la torta de casabe que su madre le había dado. Luego rezó una oración a Yucaju, el gran dios del pueblo taíno.

—¡Yucaju, que vives en el cielo, concédeme que encuentre pronto el alto caimoní!

taíno—tah•ée•noh

The next day as he walked through the forest, Niguayona found a beautiful anona fruit lying under a pile of leaves.

"How delicious it looks!" he thought. But he did not eat it. Instead, he placed it carefully in his bag. "If I don't find the caimoni fruit, perhaps I could touch the anona to Atariba's lips."

Another day passed, and Niguayona still did not find the caimoni tree. He was becoming very tired. The forest thorns tore his skin. The cassava cake was all gone, and he was hungry.

He walked on until he came to a wide, deep river, which blocked his way. Thinking of Atariba, he sat down on the riverbank and began to cry. "How can I find the caimoni now?" he asked himself.

Al día siguiente, mientras atravesaba el bosque, Niguayona encontró una hermosa fruta, anona, debajo de un montón de hojas.

—¡Qué rica se ve!— pensó. Pero en vez de comérsela, la puso con mucho cuidado en su morral.—Si no encuentro la fruta del caimoní, tal vez pueda poner la anona sobre los labios de Atariba.

Otro día pasó, y Niguayona todavía no encontraba el caimoní. Se estaba cansando mucho. Las espinas del bosque arañaban su piel. La torta de casabe se le había acabado y tenía hambre.

Siguió caminando hasta que llegó a un río ancho y profundo que interrumpía su paso. Pensando en Atariba, se sentó a la orilla del río y comenzó a llorar.—¿Ahora cómo podré encontrar el caimoní?—se preguntó a sí mismo.

anona—an•nóh•na

After a while Niguayona bravely dried his tears. Then he saw a shining light beside him. It was the anona. "I will light your path from the sky," she said.

The anona rose high above the treetops and shone over the entire forest. Higher and higher she rose until she became a majestic comet in the sky.

Then the river spoke to Niguayona. "Leap on my back," said the river. And the boy leapt on the river's back and sailed across the wide, deep water as a canoe moves, faster than the wind.

When Niguayona landed on the far side of the river, he ran toward the tall caimoni tree which was growing on the edge of the forest. He climbed to the top of the tree and plucked a red fruit from the highest branch. Then he mounted the smiling water once again and was carried quickly to the very riverbank where he had once walked with Atariba.

Después de un rato, Niguayona valientemente secó sus lágrimas. Entonces vio a su lado una luz que brillaba. Era la anona.—Yo alumbraré tu camino desde el cielo—dijo ella.

La anona se elevó por arriba de las copas de los árboles e iluminó el bosque entero. Siguió elevándose hasta que se convirtió en un majestuoso cometa en el cielo.

Entonces el mismo río le habló a Niguayona.—Salta sobre el lomo de mis aguas—le dijo el río. El muchacho saltó sobre el lomo del río y atravesó las aguas anchas y profundas, moviéndose como una canoa, más rápidamente que el viento.

Cuando Niguayona llegó al otro lado del río, corrió hacia el alto caimoní que crecía a la orilla del bosque. Trepó hasta la copa del árbol y cortó una fruta roja de la rama más alta. Luego volvió a montar el agua sonriente y fue llevado rápidamente hasta la misma orilla donde una vez había caminado con Atariba.

The people of the village were waiting for Niguayona. Day and night they had prayed to the great god Yucaju for his safe return. They had eaten nothing since his departure so that their prayers might have more power.

"Hurry, Niguayona!" they cried. "Atariba is dying!"

Niguayona raced to the village and breathlessly approached Atariba's still body. He touched the fruit to her lips which were burning with fever.

For a moment, nothing happened. Then life began to return to Atariba's little body. She moaned and opened her eyes. Slowly she sat up and looked around her.

"The caimoni must contain the blood of the gods," whispered the people.

Las gentes del pueblo esperaban a Niguayona. Habían rezado día y noche al gran dios Yucajú para que regresara sano y salvo. No habían comido nada desde que él había partido para darle más poder a sus oraciones.

—¡Ven aprisa, Niguayona!—gritaron. —¡Atariba se está muriendo!

Niguayona corrió hacia el pueblo y se acercó jadeante al cuerpo inmóvil de Atariba. Puso la fruta sobre sus labios, que ardían de fiebre.

Por un momento nada pasó. Luego, el cuerpecito de Atariba empezó a cobrar vida. Se quejó y abrió los ojos. Lentamente se sentó y miró alrededor suyo.

—El caimoní debe contener la sangre de los dioses—susurró la gente.

After Atariba recovered, there was a fiesta with many songs and dances in praise of the gods. And once again Atariba and Niguayona wandered together along the riverbank.

With the passing of time, Atariba and Niguayona became strong and compassionate leaders of the Taino people of Puerto Rico. Their story is remembered to this day.

Después que Atariba mejoró hubo una fiesta con muchas canciones y bailes para alabar a los dioses. Y Atariba y Niguayona volvieron a pasear por la orilla del río.

Con el paso del tiempo, Atariba y Niguayona llegaron a ser líderes poderosos y compasivos del pueblo taíno de Puerto Rico. Su historia se recuerda hasta hoy en día.

THINKING ABOUT IT

1 This is a tale that people have shared for many years. What will you remember about it?

2 Niguayona had a difficult task, but he received help along the way. Who helped him? How did they help him?

3 There are many tales about a person who helps someone else. Make up a tale like that.

Lon Po Po

A RED-RIDING HOOD STORY FROM CHINA

TRANSLATED AND ILLUSTRATED BY
ED YOUNG

Once, long ago, there was a woman who lived alone in the country with her three children, Shang, Tao, and Paotze. On the day of their grandmother's birthday, the good mother set off to see her, leaving the three children at home.

Before she left, she said, "Be good while I am away, my heart-loving children; I will not return tonight. Remember to close the door tight at sunset and latch it well."

But an old wolf lived nearby and saw the good mother leave. At dusk, disguised as an old woman, he came up to the house of the children and knocked on the door twice: bang, bang.

Shang, who was the eldest, said through the latched door, "Who is it?"

"My little jewels," said the wolf, "this is your grandmother, your Po Po."

"Po Po!" Shang said. "Our mother has gone to visit you!"

The wolf acted surprised. "To visit me? I have not met her along the way. She must have taken a different route."

"Po Po!" Shang said. "How is it that you come so late?"

The wolf answered, "The journey is long, my children, and the day is short."

Shang listened through the door. "Po Po," she said, "why is your voice so low?"

"Your grandmother has caught a cold, good children, and it is dark and windy out here. Quickly open up, and let your Po Po come in," the cunning wolf said.

Tao and Paotze could not wait. One unlatched the door and the other opened it. They shouted, "Po Po, Po Po, come in!"

At the moment he entered the door, the wolf blew out the candle.

"Po Po," Shang asked, "why did you blow out the candle? The room is now dark."

The wolf did not answer.

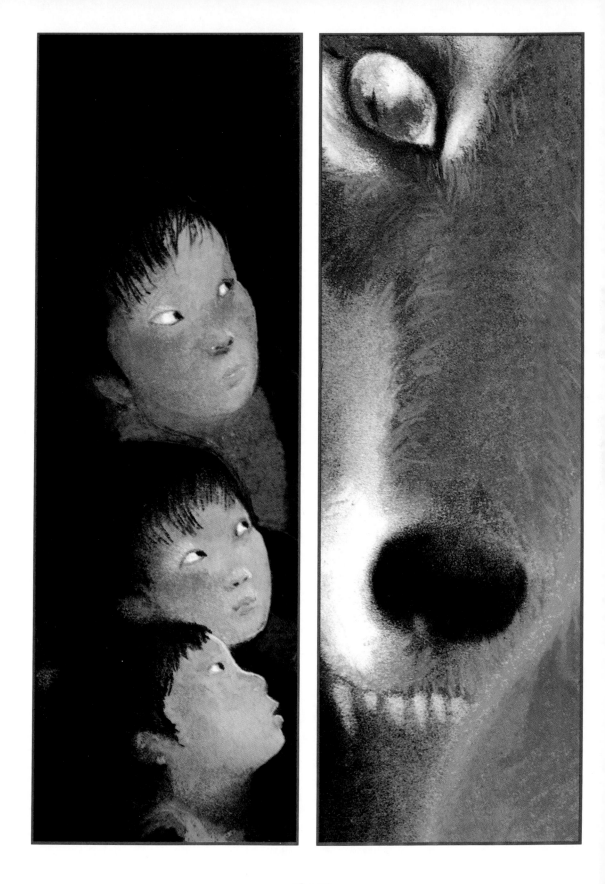

F•123

Tao and Paotze rushed to their Po Po and wished to be hugged. The old wolf held Tao. "Good child, you are so plump." He embraced Paotze. "Good child, you have grown to be so sweet."

Soon the old wolf pretended to be sleepy. He yawned. "All the chicks are in the coop," he said. "Po Po is sleepy too." When he climbed into the big bed, Paotze climbed in at one end with the wolf, and Shang and Tao climbed in at the other.

But when Shang stretched, she touched the wolf's tail. "Po Po, Po Po, your foot has a bush on it."

"Po Po has brought hemp strings to weave you a basket," the wolf said.

Shang touched grandmother's sharp claws. "Po Po, Po Po, your hand has thorns on it."

"Po Po has brought an awl to make shoes for you," the wolf said.

At once, Shang lit the light and the wolf blew it out again, but Shang had seen the wolf's hairy face.

"Po Po, Po Po," she said, for she was not only the eldest, she was the most clever, "you must be hungry. Have you eaten gingko nuts?"

"What is gingko?" the wolf asked.

"Gingko is soft and tender, like the skin of a baby. One taste and you will live forever," Shang said, "and the nuts grow on the top of the tree just outside the door."

The wolf gave a sigh. "Oh, dear. Po Po is old, her bones have become brittle. No longer can she climb trees."

"Good Po Po, we can pick some for you," Shang said.

The wolf was delighted.

Shang jumped out of bed and Tao and Paotze came with her to the gingko tree. There, Shang told her sisters about the wolf and all three climbed up the tall tree.

The wolf waited and waited. Plump Tao did not come back. Sweet Paotze did not come back. Shang did not come back, and no one brought any nuts from the gingko tree. At last the wolf shouted, "Where are you, children?"

"Po Po," Shang called out, "we are on the top of the tree eating gingko nuts."

"Good children," the wolf begged, "pluck some for me."

"But Po Po, gingko is magic only when it is plucked directly from the tree. You must come and pluck it from the tree yourself."

The wolf came outside and paced back and forth under the tree where he heard the three children eating the gingko nuts at the top. "Oh, Po Po, these nuts are so tasty! The skin so tender," Shang said. The wolf's mouth began to water for a taste.

Finally, Shang, the eldest and most clever child, said, "Po Po, Po Po, I have a plan. At the door there is a big basket. Behind it is a rope. Tie the rope to the basket, sit in the basket and throw the other end to me. I can pull you up."

The wolf was overjoyed and fetched the basket and the rope, then threw one end of the rope to the top of the tree. Shang caught the rope and began to pull the basket up and up.

Halfway she let go of the rope, and the basket and the wolf fell to the ground.

"I am so small and weak, Po Po," Shang pretended. "I could not hold the rope alone."

"This time I will help," Tao said. "Let us do it again."

The wolf had only one thought in his mind: to taste a gingko nut. He climbed into the basket again. Now Shang and Tao pulled the rope on the basket together, higher and higher.

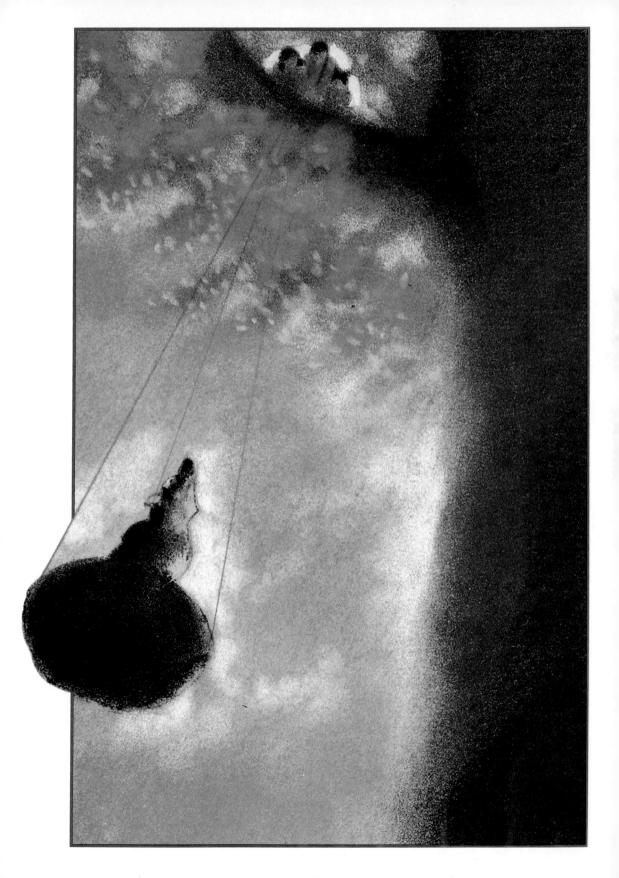

F•129

Again, they let go, and again the wolf tumbled down, down, and bumped his head.

The wolf was furious. He growled and cursed. "We could not hold the rope, Po Po," Shang said, "but only one gingko nut and you will be well again."

"I shall give a hand to my sisters this time," Paotze, the youngest, said. "This time we shall not fail."

Now the children pulled the rope with all of their strength. As they pulled they sang, "Hei yo, hei yo," and the basket rose straight up, higher than the first time, higher than the second time, higher and higher and higher until it nearly reached the top of the tree. When the wolf reached out, he could almost touch the highest branch.

But at that moment, Shang coughed and they all let go of the rope, and the basket fell down and down and down. Not only did the wolf bump his head, but he broke his heart to pieces.

"Po Po," Shang shouted, but there was no answer.

"Po Po," Tao shouted, but there was no answer.

"Po Po," Paotze shouted. There was still no answer. The children climbed to the branches just above the wolf and saw that he was truly dead. Then they climbed down, went into the house, closed the door, locked the door with the latch and fell peacefully asleep.

F•131

On the next day, their mother returned with baskets of food from their real Po Po, and the three sisters told her the story of the Po Po who had come.

Pulling the Theme Together
COURAGE

1 You are a baby-sitter reading *Lon Po Po* to some young children. How will you read it to keep their attention? How will you help them enjoy the pictures?

2 Think back over the selections in this book. Which are old stories? New stories? Nonfiction? Poems? Which selections will you recommend most of all? Why?

3 The characters in this book get together for an important assembly. One of them is to be given a blue ribbon for outstanding courage. Who should receive the ribbon? Why?

Books to Enjoy

Pioneers
by Martin W. Sandler
HarperCollins, 1994
Meet some of the most heroic figures from America's past—the men, women, and children who braved treacherous rivers, dust storms, prairie fires, poorly marked trails, and other dangers to settle the American West.

The Seal Oil Lamp
by Dale DeArmond
Little, Brown, 1988
The Eskimo village tells Allugua's family that he must be left behind because of his blindness. He is left with just some oil for his lamp, and a bit of food.

A Matter of Pride
by Emily Crofford
Carolhoda, 1991
Meg makes fun of her mother's worries until she realizes that sometimes bravery means overcoming our greatest fears.

From Anna
by Jean Little
HarperCollins, 1972
Anna doesn't know why she is clumsy and slow until her family finds out she needs eyeglasses. With her glasses and her new friends, she must prove to herself that she is able to learn.

Diego Rivera

by Jan Gleiter and Kathleen Thompson
Illustrations by Yoshi Miyake
Raintree, 1989
Mexican artist Diego Rivera painted huge, colorful murals to show his support for the hard-working poor.

A Tournament of Knights

written and illustrated by Joe Lasker
HarperCollins, 1989
Lord Justin must prove to his father that he has the right to become a knight. He challenges Sir Rolf to a duel in front of the entire kingdom.

The Lighthouse Keeper's Daughter

by Arielle North Wilson
Little, Brown, 1987
Miranda's family is new to the hard island life at the lighthouse. When Miranda's father is stranded, she must keep the lights burning to protect her family and sailors at sea.

The Hundred Dresses

by Eleanor Estes
Harcourt, Brace, 1974
Everyone laughs at Wanda's story of having a hundred dresses in her closet. Maddie finally stands up for Wanda, but she wonders if it's too late.

Literary Terms

Folk tale

Some folk tales concern people's wishes and needs. *Atariba & Niguayona* is a Puerto Rican folk tale with this theme. *Lon Po Po* is a Chinese folk tale that is similar to *Little Red Riding Hood.* It tells of the struggle between good (the children) and evil (the wolf).

Narrative Nonfiction

Narrative nonfiction tells a true story. *Teammates* tells about the career of a famous baseball player, Jackie Robinson, who was treated badly because of his race, and his friendship with another great player, Pee Wee Reese. Although the information in the book is told in story form, it is all true.

Personal Essay

A **personal essay** is a person's account of something interesting or important to the person's life. "About *Nadia the Willful*" is a personal essay because it tells how an incident in the author's life led to her writing the story.

Rhythm

Every poem has **rhythm,** the pattern of sounds in speech and writing. As you read the first line of "About the Teeth of Sharks," notice how you stress these words: "The thing about a shark is— teeth." The way you say the words gives the poem rhythm.

Setting

An author tries to describe the setting of a story so clearly that readers feel that they are there. *Nadia the Willful* takes place in the desert where the Bedouin live. The first line tells of "the land of the drifting sands." That is a powerful description. Illustrations show sand, palm trees, the clothing of these desert people, and their striped tents. All of these details establish the setting of the story.

Suspense

Night of the Twisters is a suspense story. The plot is built around conflict between people and nature. Notice the signs that the tornadoes are coming closer—shingles flapping overhead, the sound of the siren, the sudden quiet, and the radio warning *Tornado Alert!* Each new sign is more frightening than the last. That is the way the author builds suspense into a story's plot.

Glossary

Vocabulary from your selections

a·dore (ə dôr′), **1** to love and admire very greatly: *She adores her mother.* **2** to like very much: *I just adored that movie!* **3** to worship: *"O! Come, let us adore Him,"* sang the choir. verb, **a·dores, a·dored, a·dor·ing.**

awl (ôl), a pointed tool used for making small holes in leather or wood: *The shoemaker used an awl to make holes for the shoelaces.* noun.

awl being used to mark places for screws on a piece of wood

ban·ish (ban′ish), **1** to force to leave a country: *The king banished some of his enemies.* **2** to force to go away; drive away: *The children banished her from their game for cheating.* verb.

bit·ter (bit′ər), **1** having a sharp, harsh, unpleasant taste: *Quinine is bitter medicine.* **2** causing pain or grief; hard to admit or bear: *a bitter defeat. The death of his father was a bitter loss.* **3** showing pain or grief: *The lost child shed bitter tears.* **4** harsh or cutting: *a bitter remark.* **5** very cold: *The bitter winter killed our apple tree.* adjective.

bit·ter·ness (bi′tər nis), the state or quality of being bitter, harsh, or unpleasant: *There was much bitterness in the small town when the factory closed down.* noun.

cease (sēs), to stop: *The music ceased suddenly.* verb, **ceas·es, ceased, ceas·ing.**

cer·ti·fied (sėr′tə fīd), declared official or correct: *Janine is a certified medical assistant.* adjective. See **certify.**

cer·ti·fy (sėr′tə fī), **1** to declare something true or correct by an official spoken, written, or printed statement: *This diploma certifies that you have completed high school.* **2** to guarantee the quality or value of: *The fire inspector certified the school building as fireproof.* verb, **cer·ti·fies, cer·ti·fied, cer·ti·fy·ing.**

com·pas·sion·ate (kəm pash′ə nit), pitying; wishing to help those that suffer: *The compassionate doctor gave free treatment to the poor.* adjective.

com·pete (kəm pēt′), to try hard to win or gain something wanted by others; take part in a contest: *She competed against many fine athletes for the gold medal. Will you compete in the final race?* verb, **com·petes, com·pet·ed, com·pet·ing.**

conch (kongk or konch), **1** a shellfish with a large, spiral shell. **2** its shell. *noun, plural* **conchs** (kongks), **conch·es** (kon′chiz).

co·ral (kôr′əl), **1** a hard substance made up of the skeletons of tiny sea animals. Red, pink, and white coral is often used for jewelry. **2** deep-pink; red. **1** *noun,* **2** *adjective.*

cough (kôf), **1** to force air from the lungs with sudden effort and noise: *Elmira coughed all night from her cold.* **2** the act or sound of coughing. **3** a condition of repeated coughing: *I had a bad cough.* **1** *verb,* **2,3** *noun.*

cre·scen·do (kre shen′dō), an increase in sound or loudness: *The music swelled to a crescendo and then died away. noun.*

cun·ning (kun′ing), **1** clever in deceiving; sly: *The cunning fox outwitted the dogs and got away.* **2** skillful or sly ways of getting what one needs or wants, or of escaping one's enemies: *The fox has a great deal of cunning.* **1** *adjective,* **2** *noun.*

cure (kyur), **1** to bring back to health; make well: *The medicine cured the sick child.* **2** to get rid of: *to cure a cold. Only great determination can cure a bad habit like smoking.* **3** something that removes or relieves a disease or a bad condition; remedy: *The scientist hoped to find a cure for the common cold.* **4** to keep bacon or other meat from spoiling by drying, salting, or other means. **1,2,4** *verb,* **cures, cured, cur·ing; 3** *noun.*

de·bris (də brē′), scattered fragments; ruins; rubbish: *The streets were covered with debris after the flood waters went down. noun.*

a hat	i it	oi oil	ch child	ə stands for:
ā age	ī ice	ou out	ng long	a in about
ä far	o hot	u cup	sh she	e in taken
e let	ō open	ù put	th thin	i in pencil
ē equal	ô order	ü rule	ᴛʜ then	o in lemon
ėr term			zh measure	u in circus

de·light (di līt′), **1** great pleasure; joy: *The children took great delight in their toys.* **2** to please greatly: *The circus delighted us.* **1** *noun,* **2** *verb.*

dike (dīk), a bank of earth or a dam built as a defense against flooding by a river or the sea: *The villagers struggled to make the dike stronger. noun.* Also spelled **dyke.**

eld·est (el′dist), oldest: *Their eldest daughter graduated from high school last year. adjective.*

ex·traor·di·nar·y (ek strôr′də ner′ē), beyond what is ordinary; very unusual; remarkable; special: *Eight feet is an extraordinary height for a person. adjective.*

debris—There were mounds of **debris** behind the houses.

fe·ver (fē′vər), **1** an unhealthy condition in which the body temperature is higher than normal (98.6 degrees Fahrenheit or 37.0 degrees Celsius in human beings): *The injured soldier had a high fever from his wound.* **2** any sickness that causes or is accompanied by fever: *scarlet fever, typhoid fever. noun.*

gate·way (gāt′wā′), **1** an opening in a wall or fence where a gate is. **2** a way to go in or out; way to get to something: *A good education can be a gateway to success. noun.*

gateway

gauge (gāj), **1** a standard measure or a scale of standard measurements. There are gauges of the thickness of wire and for the distance between the rails on railroads. **2** an instrument for measuring: *I used a gauge to find out if my bicycle tires needed more air.* **3** to measure accurately. **4** to estimate; judge. **1,2** *noun,* **3,4** *verb,* **gaug·es, gauged, gaug·ing.**

grief (grēf), great sadness caused by trouble or loss; deep sorrow: *When her father died, Marla wondered if her grief would ever end. noun.*

guard (gärd), **1** to watch over; take care of; keep safe; defend: *The dog guarded the child day and night.* **2** to keep from escaping; check; hold back: *Guard the prisoners. Guard your tongue.* **3** a person or group that protects or watches. A soldier or group of soldiers protecting a person or place is a guard. **4** to take precautions. **5** anything that gives protection; arrangement to give safety. **6** careful watch. **7** a player at either side of the center in football. **8** either of two basketball players who usually play near the center of the court on offense. **1,2,4** *verb,* **3,5-8** *noun.*

hemp (hemp), a tall plant of Asia whose tough fibers are made into heavy string, rope, and coarse cloth. *noun.*

hu·mil·i·ate (hyü mil′ē āt), lower the pride, dignity, or self-respect of: *We felt humiliated by our failure. They humiliated me by criticizing me in front of my friends. verb,* **hu·mil·i·at·ed, hu·mil·i·at·ing.**

hu·mil·i·a·tion (hyü mil′ē ā′shən), a lowering of pride, dignity, or self-respect: *After bragging about my skiing, I suffered the humiliation of falling many times. noun.*

ink·y (ing′kē), **1** like ink; dark; black: *Until the moon rose, the night was inky black.* **2** covered or stained with ink. *adjective,* **ink·i·er, ink·i·est.**

in·sep·ar·a·ble (in sep′ər ə bəl), not able to be separated: *The two dogs were inseparable companions. adjective.*

latch (lach), **1** a catch for fastening a door, gate, or window, often one not needing a key. It consists of a movable piece of metal or wood that fits into a notch or opening. **2** to fasten with a latch: *Latch the door.* **1** *noun, plural* **latch·es; 2** *verb.*

me·te·or·ol·o·gist (mē′tē ə rol′ə jist), an expert in meteorology. *noun.*

me·te·or·ol·o·gy (mē′tē ə rol′ə jē), the science that deals with weather and the atmosphere. Meteorology includes the study of atmospheric conditions such as wind, moisture, and temperature. Weather forecasts are also part of meteorology. *noun.*

o·a·sis (ō ā′sis), a place in the desert where there is water and where trees and plants can grow: *The travelers stopped at the oasis to fill their water containers. noun. plural* **o·a·ses** (ō ā′sēz′).

pluck (pluk), **1** to pick; pull off: *He plucked flowers in the garden.* **2** to pull; pull at; tug; jerk: *She plucked*

a hat	i it	oi oil	ch child	ə stands for:
ā age	ī ice	ou out	ng long	a in about
ä far	o hot	u cup	sh she	e in taken
e let	ō open	u̇ put	th thin	i in pencil
ē equal	ô order	ü rule	ᴛʜ then	o in lemon
ėr term			zh measure	u in circus

at the loose threads of her coat. **3** the act of picking or pulling. **4** to pull on the strings of a musical instrument; play by picking at the strings: *She was plucking the banjo softly.* **5** to pull the feathers out of: *to pluck a chicken before cooking it.* **1,2,4,5** *verb,* **3** *noun.*

plump (plump), pleasantly round and full: *The plump little puppy ate almost constantly. adjective.*

plunge (plunj), **1** to throw or thrust with force into a liquid or into a place: *Plunge your hand into the water.* **2** to throw oneself into water, danger, or a fight: *She plunged into the lake to save the drowning swimmer.* **3** to fall or move suddenly downward: *The plane plunged toward earth.* **4** a jump or thrust; dive: *The diver plunged from the cliff into the sea.* **1-3** *verb,* **plung·es, plunged, plung·ing; 4** *noun.*

oasis

praise (prāz), **1** a saying that a thing or person is good; words that tell the worth or value of a thing or person: *Everyone heaped praise upon the winning team.* **2** to speak well of: *The coach praised the team for its fine playing.* **3** to worship in words or song: *to praise God.* **1** *noun,* **2,3** *verb,* **prais·es, praised, prais·ing.**

pre·pare (pri per′ *or* pri par′), to make ready; get ready: *Cal prepared a book report for English class. verb,* **pre·pares, pre·pared, pre·par·ing.**

pres·sure (presh′ər), **1** the continued action of a weight or force: *The small box was flattened by the pressure of the heavy book on it.* **2** the force per unit of area: *There is a pressure of 20 pounds to the square inch on this tire.* **3** stress; strain: *I don't work well under pressure.* **4** a forceful influence: *I was under pressure from the others to change my mind.* **5** to force or urge by exerting pressure: *The car dealer tried to pressure my parents into buying a car.* **1-4** *noun,* **5** *verb,* **pres·sures, pres·sured, pres·sur·ing.**

prop·er (prop′ər), **1** right for the occasion; fitting: *Night is the proper time to sleep.* **2** in the strict sense of the word: *Puerto Rico is not part of the United States proper.* **3** decent; respectable: *proper conduct. adjective.*

pun·ish (pun′ish), **1** cause pain, loss, or discomfort to for some fault or offense: *The parents punished the naughty children.* **2** cause pain, loss, or discomfort for: *The law punishes crime. verb.*

pun·ish·ment (pun′ish mənt), **1** a punishing; being punished: *Judges determine punishment for crimes that are committed.* **2** a penalty given for a fault or offense: *Her punishment for stealing was a year in prison. noun.*

re·cov·er (ri kuv′ər), **1** to get back something lost, taken away, stolen, or sent out: *After the argument, I needed time to recover my temper. The police recovered the stolen car.* **2** to make up for something lost or damaged: *I hurried, trying to recover lost time.* **3** to get well; get back to a normal condition: *She is recovering from a cold. verb.*

route—The **route** winds through a forest.

route (rüt *or* rout), **1** a way to go; road: *Will you go to the coast by the northern route?* **2** to send by a certain way or road: *The signs routed us around the construction work and over a side road.* **3** a fixed, regular course or area of a person making deliveries or sales: *a newspaper route, a milk route.* **1,3** *noun,* **2** *verb,* **routes, rout·ed, rout·ing.**

seep (sēp), to leak slowly; trickle; ooze: *Water seeps through sand.* verb.

seg·re·ga·tion (seg′rə gā′shən), the separation of people of different races, especially in schools, restaurants, and other public places. The United States Supreme Court ruled in 1954 that segregation in public schools is unconstitutional. *noun.*

sheik (shēk), an Arab chief or head of a family, village, or tribe. *noun.*

si·ren (sī′rən), a device that makes a loud, shrill sound: *A police car went past with its siren wailing and lights flashing. noun.*

snor·kel (snôr′kəl), **1** a shaft for taking in air and discharging gases, which allows submarines to remain underwater for a very long time. It is like a periscope in shape. **2** a curved tube which enables swimmers to breathe under water while swimming near the surface. *noun.*

stern (stèrn), **1** severe; strict; harsh: *Our teacher's stern frown silenced us.* **2** hard; not yielding; firm; *stern necessity. adjective.*

stern·ly (stèrn′lē), in a stern or harsh manner: *The general sternly ordered his troops not to retreat.* adverb. See **stern.**

stout (stout), **1** fat and large: *That boy could run faster if he weren't so stout.* **2** strongly built; firm; strong: *The fort has stout walls.* **3** brave; bold: *Robin Hood was a stout fellow. adjective.*

a hat	i it	oi oil	ch child	ə stands for:
ā age	ī ice	ou out	ng long	a in about
ä far	o hot	u cup	sh she	e in taken
e let	ō open	ù put	th thin	i in pencil
ē equal	ô order	ü rule	ᴛʜ then	o in lemon
ėr term			zh measure	u in circus

twist·er (twis′tər), a whirlwind; tornado. *noun.*

twister—Enid, Oklahoma, June 6, 1966.

will·ful (wil′fəl), **1** wanting or taking one's own way; stubborn: *Ralph had a willful character and liked to disagree with almost everyone.* **2** intended; done on purpose: *willful murder, willful waste. adjective.*

Acknowledgments

Text

Page 6: From *Night of the Twisters* by Ivy Ruckman. Copyright © 1984 by Ivy Ruckman. Reprinted by permission of HarperCollins Publishers.

Page 32: "Writing *Night of the Twisters*" by Ivy Ruckman. Copyright © by Ivy Ruckman, 1991.

Page 38: "About the Teeth of Sharks" from *You Read to Me, I'll Read to You* by John Ciardi. Copyright 1962 by John Ciardi. Reprinted by permission of HarperCollins Publishers.

Page 40: "Courage" by Emily Hearn from *Hockey Cards and Hopscotch*. Copyright © 1971. Reprinted by permission of Nelson Canada, A Division of Thomson Canada Limited.

Page 41: "In the Dark of Night" by Aileen Fisher from *Cricket in a Thicket*. Copyright 1963 by Aileen Fisher. Reprinted by permission of the author.

Page 42: "A Leak in the Dike" from *Folk Tale Plays Round the World* by Paul T. Nolan, pp. 83-93. Copyright 1982 by Paul T. Nolan. Reprinted by permission of Plays, Inc.

Page 60: "Ready, Set, Dive" from *Night Dive* by Ann McGovern. Text copyright © 1984 Ann McGovern. Reprinted by permission of Simon & Schuster Books for Young Readers.

Page 74: *Teammates* by Peter Golenbock. Copyright 1990 by Peter Golenbock. Reprinted by permission of Harcourt Brace Jovanovich, Inc.

Page 82: *Teammates* by Peter Golenbock, Illustrations by Paul Bacon. Copyright © 1990 by Golenbock Communications, Illustrations © 1990 by Paul Bacon. Reprinted by permission of Harcourt Brace & Company.

Page 86: From *Nadia the Willful* by Sue Alexander, illustrated by Lloyd Bloom. Text copyright 1983 by Sue Alexander, illustrations copyright 1983 by Lloyd Bloom. Reprinted by permission of Pantheon Books, a division of Random House, Inc.

Page 102: "About *Nadia the Willful*" by Sue Alexander. Copyright by Sue Alexander, 1991.

Page 106: *Atariba & Niguayona* adapted by Harriet Rohmer & Jesús Guerrero Rea. Illustrated by Consuelo Méndez. Copyright © 1976, 1988 by Children's Book Press. Reprinted by permission of GRM Associates, Inc., Agents for Children's Book Press.

Page 120: *Lon Po Po, A Red-Riding Hood Story from China,* translated and illustrated by Ed Young. Copyright 1989 by Ed Young. Reprinted by permission of Philomel Books.

Artists

Illustrations owned and copyrighted by the illustrator.
Bob Gleason cover, 1, 3
Bill Vuksanovich 6, 14, 19, 37, (details: 8, 12, 15, 16, 21, 26, 31)
Fran Vuksanovich 16-17, 24-25, 29-30, (border: 8-13, 15-18, 20-29, 34-36)
Rick Kroninger 32, 82
John Holm 4, 38-39
Byron Gin 40-41
Joanne Scribner 4, 42-59
Lloyd Bloom 86-101, 137 (border: 102, 104-105)
Harry Roolaart 102
Consuelo Méndez 5, 106-119
Ed Young 120-132, 133

Photographs

Unless otherwise acknowledged, all photographs are the property of ScottForesman.
Page 32: Courtesy Stuart Ruckman
Page 60: John Payne
Pages 61, 73 (top): Richard Surman/Tony Stone Worldwide
Pages 62, 66 (top), 71: Al Grotell
Pages 65, 69: Norbert Wu
Page 66 (bottom): Patrice Ceisel/John G. Shedd Aquarium
Pages 67, 69, 72: Naval Photographic Center
Page 73 (bottom) Paul Humann/Jeffrey L. Rotman
Pages 74, 76, 80, 136: FPG
Page 82: Courtesy Peter Golenbock
Page 84: National Baseball Library
Page 85: Steven Curtis
Page 102: Courtesy Sue Alexander
Page 140: Ellis Herwig/Stock Boston
Page 141: Cathy Koehler
Page 142: Backgrounds/West Light
Page 143: NSSL/NDAA

Glossary

The contents of the glossary have been adapted from *Beginning Dictionary*, Copyright © 1988 Scott, Foresman and Company.